Reading

for Christian Schools® 3-2

Bob Jones University Press, Greenville, South Carolina 29614

Consultants

from the administration and faculty of Bob Jones University

Grace C. Collins, Ph.D., *Chairman, Department of Linguistics*
Walter G. Fremont, Ed.D., *Dean of the School of Education*
Melva M. Heintz, M.A., *Elementary Principal*
Janice A. Joss, M.A.T., *Graduate School of Education*
Betty Anne Rupp, M.A., *Professor of Reading, School of Education*
Philip D. Smith, Ed.D., *Provost*
Hazel M. Truman, M.A., *Project Director, University Press*

READING for Christian Schools® 3-2

Produced in cooperation with the Bob Jones University School of Education and Bob Jones Elementary School.

ISBN 0-89084-222-1

©1983 Bob Jones University Press
Greenville, South Carolina 29614

A careful effort has been made to trace the ownership of selections included in this anthology in order to secure permission to reprint copyright material and to make full acknowledgement of their use. If any error of omission has occurred, it is purely inadvertent and will be corrected in subsequent editions, provided written notification is made to the publisher.

Alfred A. Knopf, Inc.: "Lullaby" from *Collected Poems,* by Robert Hillyer. Copyright 1933 and renewed 1961 by Robert Hillyer. Copyright ©1961 by Robert Hillyer. Reprinted by permission of Alfred A. Knopf, Inc.

E. P. Dutton & Co, Inc.: "Daniel Boone" from *I Sing the Pioneer,* by Arthur Guiterman, copyright 1926 by E. P. Dutton and renewed 1954 by Viola Linda Guiterman. Reprinted by permission of Louise H. Sclove.

E. P. Dutton & Co., Inc.: "Forgiven" from *Now We Are Six,* by A. A. Milne, copyright 1927 by E. P. Dutton, copyright renewed 1955 by A. A. Milne. Reprinted by permission of the publisher.

Harper & Row, Publishers, Inc.: "André" from *Bronzeville Boys and Girls,* by Gwendolyn Brooks. Copyright ©1956 by Gwendolyn Brooks Blakely. Reprinted by permission of Harper & Row, Publishers, Inc.

Houghton Mifflin Company: Glossary material based on the lexical database of the *Children's Dictionary,* copyright ©1981 Houghton Mifflin Company. No part of this book may be reproduced or transmitted in any form or by any means, electronic or mechanical, including photocopying and recording, or by any information storage or retrieval system, except as may be expressly permitted by the 1976 Copyright Act or with prior written permission from both Houghton Mifflin Company and the Bob Jones University Press.

20   19   18   17   16   15   14   13   12

CONTENTS

Treasures

A New Land

Creatures Great and Small

TREASURES

The Valentine's Day Surprises

An old yellow school bus jolted down the bumpy South Texas road. On each side of the road stretched endless, flat fields. In the fields dried grasses huddled in clumps against the winter rain.

Inside the bus, nine-year-old María Martínez shivered and gripped the edge of the seat with one hand. With the other hand she clutched two books, a shoe box covered with paper hearts, and a brown grocery bag.

María's younger brother, Carlos, sat beside the window. He blew on the cold glass. Then he drew a crooked airplane in the frosty mist with the tip of his finger.

"Do you want to see my valentines?" María asked.

"Maybe when we get home," said Carlos. He turned toward María. "I can't wait until tonight. What kind of cake mix did Jenny's mom get?"

"Angel food," María replied. "She bought everything on my list—angel food cake mix, frosting, and candy hearts."

"M-mm, angel food, my favorite! Did she have enough money?" asked Carlos.

"Yes, but it took almost all of our three dollars," María said. "We don't have much left."

"Do you think Señor and Señora Sanchez will be surprised?" asked Carlos.

"I hope so. Wouldn't it be wonderful if they were so happy that they adop . . . ?" María began, then stopped.

"If they did what?" asked Carlos.

"Nothing. Forget it," María said.

"Come on, María. Tell me," begged Carlos. He tugged on María's coat sleeve and stared into her big brown eyes.

María just smiled and shook her head. She thought, "I can't tell my secret dream to anyone, not even to Carlos. If I can just make our foster parents happy, they might keep us. Then Carlos and I would have a real family."

The rain had slowed to a drizzle by the time the rattling bus stopped beside the Sanchezes' driveway. When the driver opened the doors, María and Carlos hurried down the aisle. They climbed down the narrow steps, splashed through a puddle of muddy water, and crossed the road in front of the bus.

Carlos flapped his arms and ran up the wet driveway, not missing a single puddle.

"Hey, wait for me!" called María.

"Quack! Quack! I'm a duck!" said Carlos. He splashed through a big puddle, then dashed into the carport.

"Carlos, don't forget to take off your shoes!" María called. She carefully walked around the puddles. Then she wiped her shoes on the mat at the entrance to the carport.

"Carlos, you could have helped me carry—"

"Whoa, there. No fighting in this house," said Mr. Sanchez as he stepped from his workshop. "How was school? Did you get many valentines?"

"I got a valentine from everyone in my class," María said proudly. "We even had cute little heart-shaped cookies and pink lemonade at our party."

"We didn't have sissy cookies and lemonade," said Carlos. "Our teacher gave us cola and thick, gooey, chocolate cupcakes."

"Carlos, did you get any valentines?" asked Mr. Sanchez.

"Look at these," said Carlos as he pulled a handful of crumpled paper from his pocket. "The boys sent me some funny ones."

Mr. Sanchez laughed at Carlos's funny valentines. Then he asked, "Didn't you get any valentines from the girls in your class?"

The Valentine's Day Surprises

Carlos blushed. "Oh, I threw those away. They were too mushy."

Mr. Sanchez ruffled Carlos's straight black hair. "You won't feel that way in a few years," he said. "By the way, Mrs. Sanchez will be a little late. She has to wait for another nurse to take her place. Why don't we go into the kitchen and fix some hot chocolate? Maybe we could even find a few marshmallows."

"But that will ruin our surprise!" said Carlos.

"What surprise?" asked Mr. Sanchez.

María frowned at her brother. "Carlos and I have planned a Valentine's Day surprise for you and Señora Sanchez. Could you stay out here for a little while longer?"

"Well, I could work on the car a little longer," said Mr. Sanchez. "Will an hour be long enough? Mrs. Sanchez fixed a casserole, and I'm supposed to put it in the oven."

"I'll put it in the oven," said María. "I've done it before."

"And I'll help," Carlos added.

Mr. Sanchez smiled. "How could I refuse two willing helpers? Okay, I'll watch for Mrs. Sanchez. Just don't burn down the house."

"We'll be careful," María promised.

"Boy, are you going to be surprised!" said Carlos.

The Trouble with Surprises

"María, do you know what you're doing?" asked Carlos. "You've never baked a cake all by yourself."

"Oh, it will be simple," María replied with confidence as she tore open the box. "Why do you think the box says it's 'super easy'? Here. Read the directions for me. What should I do first?"

Carlos took the box and read, "Heat o . . . oven to 350 something."

"350 degrees," said María. "What's next?"

"We need a tube cake pan," Carlos said.

María looked at the shelves that held the pots and pans. She carefully searched each shelf once . . . then twice. There was no tube cake pan.

"We'll just have to use two round cake pans," she decided. "They work for other cakes. We must hurry," María said, looking at the kitchen clock. "What's the next step?"

"Blend in large . . . mixer bowl on low speed . . . thirty sec . . . onds . . . ," read Carlos.

"What do I blend?" asked María.

"Let me finish reading," said Carlos. "Cake mix. Eleven and three cups water. Three—"

"Wait!" said María. "Eleven and three cups water? That's too much."

"See for yourself," said Carlos. He held out the box and pointed to the second ingredient: 1 1/3 cups water.

"That's one and one-third cups water," explained María. "I'll measure the water while you open the mix."

After María had measured the water and added it to the mix, she asked, "Okay, what's next?"

"Three egg whites," said Carlos. "I already looked. We don't have any."

María opened the refrigerator door and took out a carton of eggs. "Sí, we have three eggs."

"The directions say three egg whites," said Carlos. "Those eggs are brown."

"The egg white isn't the color of the shell," María explained. "It's the clear part inside the shell. Watch. I'll show you."

María took out an egg and gently tapped it against the rim of the mixing bowl. When the shell split apart, she caught the yellow egg yolk in her left hand. The clear egg white dripped through her fingers into the mixing bowl.

"See. It's easy," María bragged.

Carlos handed another egg to his sister. "Try this one."

María cracked the second egg against the rim of the mixing bowl. As she caught the yolk, her thumb poked the soft ball. Yellow egg yolk and clear egg white dripped through her fingers.

"Was that supposed to happen?" Carlos asked.

"Oh, it won't hurt the cake," María decided. She added another egg, yolk and all, pushed the carton to one side, and asked, "What's next?"

Carlos looked at the box. "Mix . . . water . . . eggs. That's all."

María lowered the beaters into the bowl. "How long do I blend this? I can't remember."

"Blend on low speed . . . thirty sec . . . onds," Carlos read. "Then beat on . . . med . . . i . . . um speed for two minutes."

"Hold this bowl for me," said María.

Carlos dropped the box on the counter and reached across for the bowl. His elbow hit the carton of eggs and sent it spinning off the counter to the floor. Carlos stared at the spreading yellow blob in horror.

"It's okay," María said. "You can clean it up."

Carlos lifted the carton out of the mess and made a face. "Yuk!"

"It doesn't feel that bad," María said encouragingly. "Pretend it's Jell-o. I'll help you when I get the mixer going."

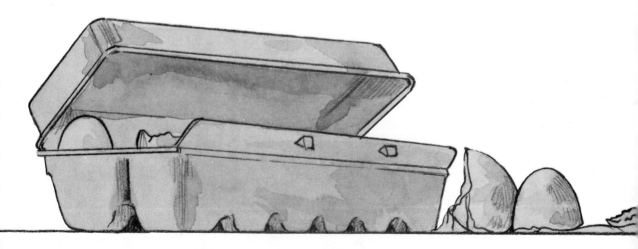

"How long . . . Oh, yes, you said two minutes." María carefully set the timer and turned on the mixer. The beaters spun and cake mix flew out of the bowl in a thin mist, raining down on Carlos's head.

"Turn it off!" he yelled. "Turn it off!"

María switched the mixer off and gave Carlos an embarrassed look. "I had it on high."

"I thought you knew how to do this," Carlos muttered, raking an egg-covered hand through his hair."

María giggled. "You'd better quit that, or we'll have to bake your hair."

Carlos jerked his hand away from his hair, slinging egg yolk and cake mix across the room.

María sighed. "We're going to have to clean this kitchen well."

This time María made sure the beaters were out of the bowl. She reset the timer, turned the mixer on low, and gently lowered the beaters into the bowl. Then when the timer stopped, she turned off the mixer and lifted the beaters out of the bowl.

When María had poured the cake batter into the two pans, she asked, "How long should the cake stay in the oven?"

"Fifty minutes," replied Carlos, still scrubbing the floor. "I think."

María reset the timer and placed the pans in the oven.

"See. I told you it would be easy to make this cake," she said.

Hearts of Love

"As soon as we get the kitchen cleaned up, we'll wash your hair," María said. "Then everything will be clean and ready."

She got a fresh cleaning cloth and helped Carlos finish cleaning the floor.

"You wipe off the refrigerator, and I'll clean the counter and put everything away," María said, handing Carlos her cloth.

Twenty minutes later the kitchen was spotless. María checked the timer. "We have plenty of time to wash your hair. Come on, Carlos."

Carlos sniffed. "María, are you sure the cake isn't done? I smell something."

"No, I just checked the timer. It still has thirty minutes to go."

"Hadn't you better look at it?"

María looked at the oven door doubtfully. "I don't think you're supposed to open the oven door while a cake is baking." She hesitated for a minute and then said, "Come on, let's do your hair. We did everything right."

They went down the hall to the bathroom. María lathered Carlos's hair and scrubbed hard.

"Ow, María," Carlos cried. "That hurts!"

"I'm sorry, Carlos, but the egg was almost dry."

María rinsed his hair and put more shampoo on it. This time she scrubbed more gently. As she was rinsing his hair, she stopped and sniffed the air. "That smells like . . . Oh no!" she cried. María threw a towel to Carlos and rushed back down the hall.

Carlos rubbed his hair and raced after María. When he reached the kitchen, María was leaning against the counter, holding her head. On the counter were two very brown cakes that looked more like huge brown mushrooms. A cloud of smoke poured from the oven door.

Carlos fanned the smoke away from his eyes. "I told you it was burning."

"Oh, look at the oven," María wailed. "The cake spilled over, and the oven is a mess!"

She leaned against the refrigerator and burst into tears.

Just then Mr. Sanchez peeked into the kitchen. "Have you been burning tires?" he asked. "Is it safe to come in?"

"Oh, come on in," said Carlos. "Our surprise is ruined."

"What's wrong?" asked Mrs. Sanchez as she followed her husband into the kitchen. "Why are you crying, María? Are you hurt?"

María just shook her head.

"Carlos, what happened?" asked Mrs. Sanchez.

"Well, we tried to bake a Valentine's Day cake for you," Carlos explained. "We wanted it to be a surprise."

"Just look at it!" María said. "It's a mess!"

"Well, it's the thought that counts," said Mrs. Sanchez. "I'm just happy that you wanted to do something special for us. Besides, the cake isn't that bad." She picked up a knife and cut through the brown crust. "Look at this. The cake is tender underneath the burned part. Why don't we cut out little hearts and cover them with frosting? Then we'll clean the oven after supper."

"Oh, no!" said María. "I didn't put the casserole in the oven. We don't have any supper."

Mrs. Sanchez put her arm around María's shoulders. "We'll just get dressed and go out to eat. When we come home, we'll fix those cakes. Maybe we'll even make some ice cream. I'm in the mood to celebrate."

"What are we celebrating?" asked María.

Mrs. Sanchez looked at her husband. "Should we tell them, Ricardo?" she asked.

Mr. Sanchez smiled and opened the door of the broom closet. He reached up to the top shelf and pulled out two heart-shaped candy boxes covered with red satin.

"Here's one for you, María," said Mr. Sanchez. "And one for you, Carlos."

María stared at the beautiful box. "It's so pretty," she said. "I've never had anything like this before."

"Aren't you going to read the card?" Mrs. Sanchez asked.

María turned the lid over. She saw an envelope taped to the inside of the lid.

"What does it say?" asked Carlos.

María pulled out the card and read, "Will you be our valentine for the rest of your life? Love always, Mom and Dad."

Carlos picked up his lid and tore open his card. "Mine says the same thing."

"What does this mean?" asked María. "Do you want Carlos and me to live here with you?"

"Forever and always," replied Mrs. Sanchez. "Would you like that?"

"But why do you want us?" asked María. "I forgot to fix supper. I burned the cake and messed up the oven."

"And sometimes María and I fight with each other," Carlos added.

Mrs. Sanchez knelt beside the two children. "María, do you stop loving Carlos when he teases you or starts a fight?"

"No. He's my brother," said María.

"Carlos, do you hate your sister when she makes mistakes?" asked Mrs. Sanchez.

"No," said Carlos.

"Well, we love you," Mrs. Sanchez said. "We love you with all your faults, and we want you to be part of our family. Would you like that?"

"Oh, sí," said María as she and Carlos hugged their new mother. "I always wanted a real family."

"What about me?" said Mr. Sanchez. "Don't I get a hug?"

The two children ran to their new father. "Thank you for our Valentine's Day surprise," said María. "It's the best surprise ever."

God Provides

When Ahab became king, he did more to provoke the Lord God of Israel than all the kings of Israel that were before him. So the Lord sent Elijah, the prophet, before Ahab to tell him that neither rain nor dew would fall until he, Elijah, announced it. And the Lord hid Elijah from Ahab's fury by the brook Cherith and sent ravens to feed him. When the brook dried up, the Lord sent Elijah to Zarephath, where a widow woman gave him food and shelter. In this way, the Lord provided for his servant, Elijah.

Heat pressed down on the dry land like a blanket, smothering the thirsty ground. Elijah pulled his cloak of camel's hair over his head to protect himself from the burning sun. In the distance he could see the walls of Zarephath.

"There will be water and food waiting for me," Elijah thought as he shook the dust from his sandals and garments. "God has said so."

As he came closer to the city, he saw a woman gathering sticks. She was dressed in the clothes of a widow. "Ah," thought Elijah. "She must be the woman of whom God spoke."

Raising his voice, he called, "I have traveled for many days without much water. Fetch me, I pray thee, a little water in a vessel, that I may drink."

The woman turned to get some water for Elijah. She had not gone far when Elijah called to her again.

"Bring me, I pray thee, a morsel of bread in thine hand."

She stopped and turned back to Elijah. "I am sorry, but I have not one cake. I have only a handful of meal in the bottom of my barrel and a little oil in a jar. I am gathering these sticks so that I may go in and cook for myself and my son. We were going to eat our last meal and die."

"Do not be afraid," said Elijah, speaking to the woman kindly. "Do as you planned, but first make me a little cake. Then bake cakes for yourself and your son. For the Lord God of Israel has said that your barrel of meal shall not be empty, nor shall the jar of oil be used up, until the day that the Lord sends rain upon the earth."

The woman picked up her sticks and hurried to do as Elijah had told her. When she made Elijah's cake, there was still oil and meal left!

And in all the years of the drought, the jar of oil was never empty and there was always enough meal for Elijah, the widow, and her son.

For three years the drought lasted. The grass disappeared from the hillsides, and the fields became wastelands. Although Ahab searched for Elijah so that he could slay him, Elijah was not to be found. He was safe in the house of the widow, waiting on the Lord.

The Widow's Jar of Oil

In Bible times, oil was both a necessity and a luxury. Olive oil could be found in the home of every family, from the richest queen to the poor widow who helped Elijah.

The oil was expensive and took a long time to make. The best oil came from olives that were picked just after they ripened and before they turned black. If the olives were picked too green, the oil would be bitter. If the olives were picked too ripe, the oil would be rancid.

Olives were crushed with a heavy stone to remove the oil. When the stone first broke the skin, much oil came from the pulp. This first oil was of the highest grade. More pressing produced oil of a cheaper grade.

Used in cooking, olive oil prevented meat or bread from sticking to the pan. Sometimes the oil was mixed with flour or meal to make bread dough or cakes similar to those that the widow fed Elijah.

The lamps in most houses burned with a wick that soaked in a small clay bowl of olive oil. In the Tabernacle the golden lampstand burned from small cups of pure olive oil.

Olive oil was also thought to promote healing. Cuts and scrapes were rubbed with the oil, and wealthy people took baths in warm olive oil. Women rubbed the oil into their skin to keep it soft. The kings of Israel were anointed with the finest olive oil available.

Because of her extreme poverty, the widow who helped Elijah probably used oil of a cheap grade. Imagine her pleasure as the Lord replenished her jar day after day with olive oil fit to anoint a king!

Elly's Secret

In the fall of 1864 Sherman began his march to the sea. Having destroyed the railroad to the rear, he was dependent on the countryside for supplies. His Union troops swept a sixty-mile-wide path as they looted and burned their way across Georgia. Bands of foragers raided outlying plantations to provide food for the huge army and destroyed anything that might be left to sustain the Confederacy.

The late November morning of 1864 made no promises of being unusual. If anything, it was quiet—too quiet. Eight-year-old Elly Pritchard wandered through the strangely bare parlor and walked out onto the side porch. Down by the cotton barn she caught a glimpse of her brothers as they dashed quickly into the shadowed doorway.

"Humph," she thought to herself. "Probably

hiding something else."

Last week when the news had come that the Yankees were in Georgia, Elly was sick in bed. Everyone had rushed around hiding anything that was of value. Frustrated, Elly had watched as much as she could from her bedroom window, shouting questions to all who hurried by. Her hoarse shouts had quickly brought Mother and Pearl to tuck her back in bed with orders not to get out again. Elly could only watch helplessly as the silver pitcher and candlesticks were whisked from her room, along with the filigree music box Papa had sent her from Atlanta.

When Elly was well and downstairs again, her questions were fended off with, "Hush, child, the less you know the better."

But this morning Elly had asked so many questions that her mother had told her a secret. It was a much better secret than where something was hidden. Elly hugged her doll tightly as she set off across the lawn to the cotton barn at the edge of the red clay fields. When she reached the barn, the doors were closed. Elly gave one of the doors a push, and it swung slowly inward, squeaking on its hinges. Elly stepped into the cool darkness.

"Tom! Jake! Where are you? I know you're in here!"

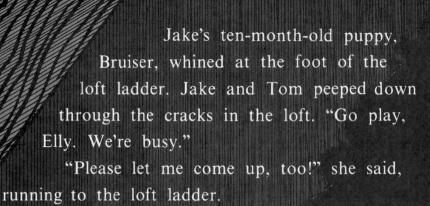

Jake's ten-month-old puppy,
Bruiser, whined at the foot of the
loft ladder. Jake and Tom peeped down
through the cracks in the loft. "Go play,
Elly. We're busy."

"Please let me come up, too!" she said,
running to the loft ladder.

"Nope," said Jake. "We have too many secret
things up here. If we let you come up, they won't
be secrets anymore."

"That's right." Tom scrambled to his knees and started counting on his fingers. "Remember the time Father brought Jake a puppy for his birthday and you told? Or the time. . ."

Elly put her hands on her hips and narrowed her eyes. "Then I won't tell you the secret I just found out from Mother."

Tom glanced at his older brother and grinned. Then both boys looked at Elly, shrugged their shoulders, and said in unison, "We don't care." Jake swung his legs over the edge of the loft and pulled out his knife while Tom put his harmonica to his lips.

Elly sighed. It was such a good secret. The boys wouldn't be sitting around if they knew. Just thinking about the secret made Elly's feelings dance like the tune on Tom's harmonica. She stooped over and petted Bruiser. If she told only two people, it would still be a secret, wouldn't it? Elly put her doll, Amanda Lyn, on the ladder and looked up at the boys. She licked her dry lips and burst out, "You would care if you knew that Father was coming home tonight!"

"He is?"

"For sure?" Jake and Tom were already scrambling down the ladder.

"Whoopee!" Both boys took off toward the house while Elly sighed. There, she had done it again. When would she learn not to tell secrets!

Bruiser, sensing the boys' excitement, leaped up, barking at Elly. Suddenly he grabbed Amanda Lyn and took off after the boys.

"Stop! Stop!" cried Elly, running after Bruiser and Amanda Lyn, who was bouncing up and down. At last, tired of the game, Bruiser gave Amanda Lyn a final shake. Glass beads scattered as he dropped the doll at Elly's feet.

With tears streaming down her cheeks, Elly picked up Amanda Lyn. The doll's blue dress was tattered and torn. Stuffing hung out of her back where Bruiser's teeth had made a three-inch rip. Sobbing, Elly cradled the doll in her arms and ran to Mother.

"There, there," said Mother, wiping away Elly's tears. "Let me see Amanda Lyn." Mother took the torn dress off and poked the stuffing back in. "Go get a new dress for Amanda Lyn and gather her beads while I sew her together."

Elly nodded and ran off. She looked in the closet, she hunted in the dresser, and she even searched under the bed. But Amanda Lyn's red dress wasn't anywhere.

"Mother will know where it is," Elly thought to herself as she ran back and burst into the sewing room.

"Oh!" Her mouth dropped open. Mother was hurriedly stuffing something that glittered into the hole in Amanda Lyn's back.

"Why are you putting your diamond necklace inside Amanda Lyn?"

Mother didn't say a word until she had sewn up the three-inch rip. Then she drew Elly close to her.

"When your father comes, he will take my jewelry to a bank in Savannah." Mother's serious gray eyes looked into Elly's blue ones. "Elly, Amanda Lyn will keep the jewels safe until tonight. It will be our secret—yours, mine, and Amanda Lyn's. Don't tell *anyone*, Elly!" Then she smiled and hugged Elly. "But remember, you and the boys are more precious to me than any jewels."

Elly nodded. The clattering of boys' boots in the hall kept her from saying more.

"Mother, Mrs. Sully's mighty sick." Jake's face was flushed from running. "Her husband wants to know if you can come right away."

Mother began gathering up her things and giving orders. "Jake, tell Pearl to fix some broth for me to take. Elly, put Amanda Lyn upstairs on your bed. Then go gather her beads and string them together. Now you children be good and obey Pearl while I'm gone."

Late that afternoon Elly sat on the back porch, stringing Amanda Lyn's glass beads together. "These beads almost look like diamonds. Amanda Lyn and I will pretend they are."

Elly tied the last knot and yawned. The sun warmed her back while the gentle breeze rustled the fall leaves as if whispering secrets.

"I've got a new secret too." Elly wiggled with delight. "But I'm not supposed to tell." She frowned. How in the world was she ever going to keep this important secret?

"Pearl's smart. I'll ask her." Elly ran upstairs and put the beads on Amanda Lyn. Then she picked up her doll and ran down to the kitchen.

"Pearl, what do you do with a secret that's just itching to pop out?"

The old woman's chuckle filled the room. "Why honey child, I just tell the Lord. He knows all the secrets of the world."

"Oh." Elly wandered back outside and sat down to think. It was comforting to know that the Lord knew Amanda Lyn's secret too. Elly hugged her doll closer.

Plop! An acorn fell from the tree, right onto her nose.

"Jake! You stop that!"

"Why?"

"I'm thinking."

"About what?"

"My new secret."

Jake dropped from the tree. "I'll let you see what's in my pocket if you'll tell me your secret."

Elly eyed his pocket, noticing a fairly large, interesting lump. But this time she did not need

someone to share her secret. She already had
Mother, Amanda Lyn, and the Lord.

Suddenly the sound of horses' hooves coming
up the long avenue broke the stillness of the fall
afternoon. Jake wasn't interested in the secret
anymore.

"Father's home!" he shouted, disappearing
around the corner of the house.

"Father's home!" Elly echoed and went running
after him. Behind her she heard pounding
footsteps which she recognized as Tom's. By the
time Elly reached the front porch, she knew it
wasn't Father that had come. Yankee soldiers were
scattering throughout the plantation at the
command of their captain. Horses whinnied,
tossing their sweaty heads. Angry shouts came
from the direction of the smokehouse.

"You won't find any hams there," she thought
with sudden pleasure. Then her face sobered as
soldiers appeared around the house, clutching
struggling chickens and turkeys. Other soldiers on
horseback were herding the servants away from
the house.

An order was shouted. "Burn that cotton!" Elly
clutched Amanda Lyn close as she saw the
stricken look on Tom's and Jake's faces. "Their
treasures were in the barn loft," she thought. Jake

ran down the steps, only to be blocked by an officer galloping by. "Jenkins!" the man called to the soldier running around the corner of the porch. "Take these children inside!"

"Yes, sir!" The soldier saluted, turned on his heel, and pointed inside. Tom grabbed Elly's hand and hurried her along behind Jake, who marched ahead of them like a soldier himself. Elly couldn't tell if Jake was scared or not. But Tom's hand was awfully clammy, and she felt her own heart beating like a drum. Elly bit her lip to keep from crying.

The soldier motioned the children into the parlor. Elly and Tom huddled close together on the couch. Jake scorned a seat, standing tall and straight.

The children watched in silent anger as the soldier went from table to table pulling open drawers and spilling their contents onto the floor. When he found nothing of value, he turned to the children. Elly shrank back at the look on his face.

"Where are your mother's jewels?" the soldier snarled, shifting his rifle in his hands.

Jake went white but didn't answer. The soldier strode across the room and grabbed Jake by the collar.

"Where are they?" he shouted, shaking the boy.

"I don't . . . know," Jake spoke between clenched teeth.

"Don't lie to me!"

While the soldier was questioning Jake, Elly clutched Amanda Lyn, unable to speak. She knew where the jewels were, but it was a secret. Mother had said not to tell . . . but Mother wouldn't want Jake hurt!

As the soldier raised his arm as if to cuff Jake soundly, Elly jumped up. "He's telling the truth. He doesn't know where they are. I didn't tell him the secret."

The soldier turned around surprised and relaxed his grip on Jake. A half smile curled his lips. "Maybe you should tell the secret to me."

Elly nodded. "Amanda Lyn has the jewels."

"A mandolin? Where?"

Slowly Elly held up her doll. The soldier's greedy eyes lit up as he saw the shimmering beads around the doll's neck.

He grabbed the doll and tore the necklace off. When he held the necklace up to the light his face grew red. His back stiffened.

"Fakes!" he yelled, throwing the beads and the doll to the floor. His whole body shook with rage as he headed for Elly.

"Soldier!" A voice barked from the doorway.

The soldier froze and turned to face his officer. "Since when do we make war on children?" snapped the officer. "Take him outside," he said to the men behind him, "and mount up. There's a Confederate regiment to the south. Move!"

With loud shouts and the sound of clattering hooves, the Yankees were gone. Outside, the children could hear the released servants trying to put out the fire.

Tom and Jake looked at Elly, who was picking up her doll.

"That was close," Jake said shakily. "Thanks Elly, but what . . ."

Tom headed for the door. "Come on, the barn's burning!"

The boys raced outside but Elly followed slowly, clutching Amanda Lyn. "I told the secret but no one understood," she whispered. "Our secret is still safe!"

Elly's mother returned to find her home and children safe. Although the year's supply of cotton was lost, enough food had been well hidden to take them through the remainder of the year. It had been Elly's father's regiment that the officer had mentioned. Elly's father did not come that night, nor the next. Elly and Amanda Lyn kept their secret until the war was over. Then when Major Pritchard returned home, Elly and Amanda Lyn were the first to greet him. The jewels that Elly had helped keep safe were sold to provide food for the Pritchards and their friends who were not as fortunate with food during the hard years following the war.

Two Crooks and Two Heroes

Act One

Narrator: One hot fourth of July, in the little town of Porcupine Hollow, more than just a parade was taking place. Our story begins at Mayor Setton's house, the home of Travis Setton. Travis and his friend, Billy Bob, have been chosen to lead the Independence Day parade.

Travis: Bye, Mom and Dad. Wave to me from the grandstand!

Mrs. Setton: We'll make sure we see you!

Mayor Setton: I'll be right proud of you two today, carrying our nation's flags. That's quite an honor.

Billy Bob: Yes, sir, Mayor Setton.

Mrs. Setton: Run along the back way, boys, down Stray Cat Alley, so you won't have to cross any streets.

Travis: Yes, ma'am.

Billy Bob: Come on, Travis. We'll be late.

Narrator: The boys left the house and turned down the alley between Taylor's Hardware and the Porcupine Hollow Bank.

Billy Bob: Mr. Taylor's closing his shop already.

Travis: The bank's closed too. But Uncle Clem must have forgotten to turn off the lights.

Billy Bob: Look, there's Uncle Clem's armored truck. I wonder why he parked it in the alley?

Travis: Probably so no one would sit on it during the parade.

Billy Bob: Uncle Clem is pretty smart.

Travis: Did you hear that noise? Something's inside Uncle Clem's truck.

Billy Bob: We'd better take a look. Give me a hand and I'll peek through the window.

Travis: See anything, Billy Bob?

Billy Bob: Leaping lizards! It's Uncle Clem, tied up like a horsefly in a spider's web! Uncle Clem! What are you doing? How'd you get in there?

Uncle Clem: Ah, uh, uh. . .

Billy Bob: The door's locked, but we'll get help, Uncle Clem. Just hold on.

Uncle Clem: Eh. . .ee. . .ou. . .

Billy Bob: Travis, you saw lights on in the bank, didn't you? I bet bank robbers did this!

Travis: You think they tied up Ol' Uncle Clem, took his keys, locked him up in the armored truck, and opened the safe?

Billy Bob: Not only that, but they're probably robbing the bank this second! Let's barricade the door so they can't get out!

Travis: If we stick this old crowbar through the door handles, they'll be stuck inside for a little while. At least 'til they can break the door down, and that will set off the alarm.

Travis: Shhh! I hear them talking.

Narrator: Inside the bank two men were emptying the vault.

Shane: Grady, get those sacks of coins and put 'em by the door. I'll clean out the drawers up front.

Grady: Sure, boss. Easy as stealin' candy from a baby.

Shane: How much longer will that take you? We've got to get out of here.

Grady: Well, boss, them bags is plenty heavy. I can't tote them too fast. It'll probably take half an hour.

Shane: Half an hour? Move it! We need to be out of here before that fool parade blocks our getaway.

Grady: Sure, boss. I'll be done before then if you say so.

Shane: I say so!

Narrator: Outside the bank door, the two boys looked at each other, wide-eyed.

Billy Bob: Come on, Travis. We don't have much time.

Travis: Shhhh. Those two sure do *sound* tough, but just wait 'til Sheriff Ridgely gets his hands on them. They'll be two sorry criminals.

Billy Bob: Let's find Sheriff Ridgely before those crooks get us, or we'll be two sorry crook-catchers locked up in the bank safe!

Act Two

Narrator: Travis and Billy Bob raced through the alley. As they reached Main Street, the parade was just starting down the street. Mrs. Sullivan was hurrying along beside the band with a worried look on her face. Deputy Slim was walking beside her, holding two flags.

Billy Bob: Travis, there's Deputy Slim. He'll know where to find Sheriff Ridgely.

Travis: Deputy Slim, Uncle Clem's been tied up and locked in his armored truck!

Billy Bob: And two robbers are stealing all the money in the bank!

Deputy Slim: Whooeeee, Sheriff Ridgely has been looking all over for you two. Now two old bank robbers are going to hold us up! And I just dropped off my paycheck at the bank this morning. Come on, boys. Sheriff Ridgely can't be too far away.

Mrs. Sullivan: Boy, boys, you're late! Get in your places. Here are your flags.

Deputy Slim: Hold the flags, boys; I'll find the sheriff.

Billy Bob: What should we do with these flags, Travis?

Travis: I don't know. We can't leave them, can we?

Narrator: The two boys and Deputy Slim were swept along with the band. As they turned the corner, they saw the sheriff on the sidewalk, trying to look in both directions at once.

Billy Bob: There's the sheriff, Deputy Slim!

Band: Crash, boom, oompah, clang, clang, boom.

Deputy Slim: Sheriff Ridgely! The bank's being robbed! Stop the parade!

Sheriff Ridgely: What?

Travis: Uncle Clem's tied up in his armored truck!

Sheriff Ridgely: Lead the way to him, boys. The parade will have to wait.

Narrator: The boys turned up Stray Cat Alley, their flags waving in the breeze. The band followed, cymbals crashing, horns tooting.

Band: Oom, oompah, crash, clang.

Billy Bob: Oh, no, Travis. The parade is following us!

Narrator: Sheriff Ridgely looked back and saw the parade. He clapped his hand to his head and groaned. Then he signaled for the band to stop playing. The parade followed them the rest of the way into the alley on tiptoe.

Travis: There's the armored truck, Sheriff. See the door to the bank? We stuck a crowbar in the handle to keep the robbers from breaking out.

Sheriff Ridgely: Good thinking, boys. All right, back up. We don't know if the robbers are armed.

Deputy Slim: Here they come now!

Billy Bob: Don't let them knock the flags down, Travis.

Narrator: The door of the bank rattled. Inside the bank someone grumbled loudly.

Shane: Grady, why did you lock this door? You knew we had to come back out this way.

Now we'll have to break out like we broke in.

Grady: Boss, I didn't lock the door. It's stuck!

Sheriff Ridgely: Come on out with your hands up!

Narrator: The sheriff removed the crowbar. Slowly the door opened and the two crooks stepped out.

Shane: We're caught again!

Band: Crash, clang, oompah!

Grady: Boss, look! Do you think they'll let us watch the parade before they throw us into jail?

Deputy Slim: Nope. It's to jail for you crooks. I'm sure Uncle Clem will want to thank Travis and Billy Bob. Let's untie him.

Sheriff Ridgely: Go ahead while I handcuff these two fellows.

Uncle Clem: Thank you, thank you. Travis and Billy Bob, you did a fine job. Give the flags to Deputy Slim and hop in my truck. I'll drive you to the grandstand. You're the heroes of the parade today!

Mrs. Sullivan: Fall in line. Follow the armored truck.

Band: Clash, clang, oompah, pah.

Narrator: The band followed the slow-moving truck through the streets to the grandstand.

Then Billy Bob and Travis took their places at the front of the line, again holding the flags.

Mrs. Sullivan: Three cheers for Travis Setton and Billy Bob Moore!

Townsfolk: Hip, hip, hooray! Hip, hip, hooray! Hip, hip hooray!

Mrs. Sullivan: Stand up tall, boys. Let those flags wave!

Mayor Setton: Come on up to the grandstand, boys. I'm as proud as a peacock. Bank robbers! Next thing I know one of you will be running for president of the United States.

Billy Bob: Yes, sir, Mayor Setton.

Townsfolk: Hip, hip, hooray!

André

I had a dream last night. I dreamed
I had to pick a Mother out.
I had to choose a Father too.
At first, I wondered what to do,
There were so many there, it seemed,
Short and tall and thin and stout.

But just before I sprang awake,
I knew what parents I would take.

And *this* surprised and made me glad:
They were the ones I always had!

Gwendolyn Brooks

Beautiful Feet

The age-old custom of binding feet to make them beautiful causes this Chinese lady to appreciate the biblical version of "beautiful feet." Her tale is an adaptation of a true story that has often been told to encourage others in faithful witnessing.

The Mission School

Tired from packing, Ming-Chu sat down on the porch of the mission school. She smiled as she listened to the shouts of the children on the playground, remembering her own first years at the mission school. Her thoughts were interrupted by the sound of running feet.

"Ming-Chu! Watch out!"

Ming-Chu looked up as a ball bounced close to her feet. Reaching down, she picked up the ball and tossed it to the bright-eyed little girl who came racing after it. "Run," Ming-Chu called.

The little girl called back over her shoulder as she ran back to the playground. "Come and watch us, Ming-Chu!"

Ming-Chu followed the running child down the path, moving slowly and carefully in her tiny shoes. At the edge of the playground she stopped to watch the game.

She giggled softly as the two leaders of the teams urged the children on to victory. One leader was the missionary, head of the mission school, and the other leader was a young Chinese man. Both men were special to Ming-Chu. The American missionary had been almost like a father to her during her years at the mission school, and the young Chinese was the man Ming-Chu was to marry. As the game ended, the two men walked toward her, still arguing cheerfully.

"Just wait until tomorrow!" challenged the missionary as they stopped beside Ming-Chu.

"You hear him, Ming-Chu?" said the young Chinese. "Another day! Always another day!"

Ming-Chu smiled. "And I will not be here to see either of you win."

The missionary turned to her. "Have you finished packing?"

"Yes," she replied. "It's hard to believe that today is my last day at the mission school."

The missionary took her hand. "Now, Ming-Chu, this is not a time for sadness. You are returning home to prepare for your wedding."

The young man nodded. "I too will miss the mission school. But I am looking forward to a new life with you, Ming-Chu. The missionary has brought the gospel to us. Now we will give the gospel to others."

As Ming-Chu smiled up at him, the porters came down the trail, carrying a sedan chair. "It is time for me to go," she said. "I will return as swiftly as possible with my family."

When the porters stopped in front of them, the young man carefully helped Ming-Chu into the sedan chair. Then he warned the porters to take special care of Ming-Chu. "I want no harm to come to my bride-to-be."

Ming-Chu laughed. "We have made the trip often. I will arrive back in one piece!"

"And in time for the wedding," the missionary said as the porters picked up the sedan chair.

"And in time for the wedding," Ming-Chu called back as the caravan began moving up the mountain trail.

Days later the caravan reached Ming-Chu's village. Children and neighbors crowded around the sedan chair as it moved slowly through the streets to Ming-Chu's house. Ming-Chu called greetings to her friends. Then the gates of her house were opened, and a servant appeared to take her to her eagerly waiting parents.

Early the next morning Ming-Chu's mother sent for the tailor. Soon material was spread across the room in a silken rainbow of bright colors.

The tailor carefully measured Ming-Chu for her wedding dress.

"Now the shoes," he said, spreading parchment on the floor. "What beautiful feet," he murmured as he traced Ming-Chu's feet on the parchment. "You must be very proud of such tiny feet."

Ming-Chu's mother beamed. "I bound her feet when she was just a baby. They are the smallest feet in the village, even smaller than my own."

Ming-Chu thought of the little girl back at the mission school who had run so lightly after the ball. What freedom the children had whose feet were not bound!

Preparations continued for the wedding trip. Soon the caravan was packed and ready to go. As Ming-Chu and her family traveled across the mountains, she watched eagerly for the first glimpse of the mission school. At last they reached the last mountain pass. There far below them lay the mission school.

"There it is!" called Ming-Chu to her parents. "We are almost there!"

A Special Gift

Ming-Chu and her family were welcomed, and the wedding festivities began. After a week of joyful celebration, Ming-Chu's family returned to their village. Ming-Chu and her new husband prepared for their first trip together into the mountains of China.

"Thank you for everything you have done for us," the two young people told the missionary. "We will miss you and will think of you often."

"May God be with you," said the missionary.

"Good-bye," called the children as Ming-Chu and her husband started down the trail, Ming-Chu in her sedan chair carried by the porters and her husband walking alongside her.

That trip was the first of many. From village to village the young people went, carrying the gospel to the Chinese. In each village Ming-Chu's husband preached, and Ming-Chu taught the women from the Bible.

The women were delighted with Ming-Chu's tiny feet, and came often to hear her teach. They began to look forward to the visits of the "lady with the beautiful feet," and many of them came to know Christ as their Saviour.

Ming-Chu enjoyed the long walks over the mountains to the different villages. As her husband walked along beside the sedan chair, Ming-Chu would read the Bible aloud.

One day she was reading a passage from Romans 10: "And how shall they preach, except they be sent? as it is written, How beautiful are the feet of them that preach the gospel of peace, and bring glad tidings of good things." Ming-Chu closed her Bible and looked along the path. It was a beautiful day, clear and crisp in early fall. "I wish I could walk with you," she said to her husband.

"There are pebbles along the path," he answered. "What if you slip and fall?"

"I would be careful to lean on you," Ming-Chu replied wistfully.

Her husband hesitated, then stopped the caravan and let her walk slowly along the path. He held her arm firmly as she walked.

"I wish my feet had never been bound," Ming-Chu said sadly. "Then I could walk easily beside you, and we would not have to travel slowly because of my sedan chair."

"But Ming-Chu," replied her husband, "you have beautiful feet!"

"No," Ming-Chu said, "you have beautiful feet."

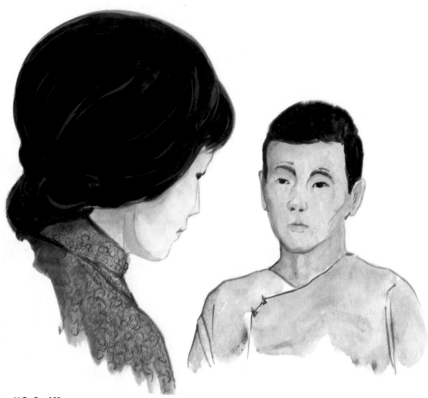

"Me!"

"Yes, you," Ming-Chu said tenderly. "The verse I just read says that the feet of those who carry the gospel to others are beautiful. That makes your feet beautiful, and mine are beautiful only because I help you, not because they are so tiny."

"I understand," said her husband. "But the Lord has used your tiny feet to bring many women to hear you teach. They come to marvel at your feet and stay to hear the gospel. The Lord uses what each of us has to further the gospel."

Ming-Chu thought for a moment as her husband helped her back into the sedan chair. "Do you know who else has beautiful feet?"

"The missionary," replied her husband, smiling at her. "He brought the gospel to us. Soon we will go back to visit him."

"I would like that very much," Ming-Chu replied.

But it was many years before they saw the missionary again. One day they received word that he was returning to the United States.

"We must go now," said Ming-Chu, "or we will never see him again."

"Yes, we will leave tomorrow," said her husband.

As Ming-Chu packed for the trip she found her little silk wedding shoes that had been carefully tucked away in a tiny box. "Husband," she said, showing him the shoes, "these shoes remind me of the verse in Romans about beautiful feet. I would like to give the shoes to the missionary."

Her husband nodded. "The little shoes will make a fine gift of remembrance."

When Ming-Chu and her husband returned to the mission, they were joyfully met by their old friends. When at last they were able to sit down with the missionary alone, Ming-Chu gave him the little shoes. She explained what beautiful feet now meant to her and asked the missionary, "Will you find some little girl in America that loves the Lord and give her these shoes? Perhaps my story will encourage her to carry the gospel to others as you have done."

When the aged missionary returned to America, he gave the tiny silk wedding shoes to an eight-year-old girl. She cherished the tiny shoes and never forgot the story of Ming-Chu's "beautiful feet." The girl grew up to serve the Lord faithfully in many ways. She still has the tiny shoes and often shows them to others. After she tells Ming-Chu's story, she encourages her listeners to be faithful in spreading the gospel so that they too may have beautiful feet.

A Snake in the House

A Pet for the Summer

"Dad! Dad!" The screen door slammed behind Tony as he ran to the driveway.

Mr. Peroni stopped the station wagon. "What a welcome," he said, smiling. "What's going on?"

"Mom said I could keep one of the classroom pets for the summer if it's all right with you," Tony said hurriedly. "We just have time to catch Mrs. Allen before she leaves."

"Hold on a minute, son." Mr. Peroni frowned. "Today's the last day of school. Why didn't we hear about this earlier?"

"I thought Paul Bartlett was going to keep Barney," Tony replied, "and all the other animals were taken. Paul's parents decided to go away for the summer, so he called me a few minutes ago. If we hurry, we can get to the school in time."

"All right, let's go," Mr. Peroni said, reaching across to open the car door for Tony. Tony slid into the seat, and Mr. Peroni backed the car out of the driveway.

"Now you're sure it's okay with your mother?"

"Yes, sir. Mom just said I would have to take care of Barney myself." Tony leaned forward, peering out the window.

Mr. Peroni slowed for the stop sign at Fifth and Oak Street. "Do you know how to care for this Barney animal?"

"Oh, yes, sir," Tony replied without taking his eyes from the road. "Snakes are easy to take care of anyway."

"Snakes?" Mr. Peroni stepped on the brake and turned to look at Tony. "Snakes? Your mother agreed to let you keep a snake?"

"In the garage, not in the house," Tony said hastily. "I promised to keep him in a cage in the garage."

Mr. Peroni shook his head, then turned left on Fifth Street. "Tony, do you know why your mother is afraid of snakes?"

"She was bitten by a snake when she was little, wasn't she?"

"Yes. She was very sick, Tony. She has been afraid of snakes ever since." Mr. Peroni turned onto Elm Street. "I want you to remember that and be careful with your snake."

"I will, Dad. Barney isn't a poisonous snake. You know the school wouldn't let us keep a dangerous snake," Tony said earnestly.

Mr. Peroni laughed. "I wouldn't think so."

He stopped the car in the school parking lot. "You run ahead and see if Mrs. Allen is still there. I'll park the car and catch up with you."

"Thanks, Dad!" Tony slid out and slammed the door.

By the time Mr. Peroni reached the classroom, Tony was hanging over a glass tank in the back. Mr. Peroni smiled at Mrs. Allen. "I see Tony reached you in time. Looks like we'll have a guest for the summer."

"You don't know how glad I am to see you!" Mrs. Allen said. "No one wanted to take Barney. I didn't know what I was going to do."

"None of the boys wanted a snake?" Mr. Peroni asked.

"Oh, the problem wasn't the boys. It was the mothers," she said, leading Mr. Peroni to the back. "A lot of people just don't care for boa constrictors."

"Boa . . ." Mr. Peroni coughed, leaning over Tony's shoulder to look at the snake coiled in the heavy tank.

"He's just a baby boa, Dad," Tony said. "Just look at him!"

"Tony, did you tell your mother that Barney is a boa constrictor?"

Tony looked up, startled. "I don't remember, Dad. I told her he was a snake and that he was a baby, but I don't remember if I said he was a boa or not. We always called him Barney here at school." He bit his lip and looked at Barney.

"I'll understand if you can't take Barney . . ." Mrs. Allen began.

"No," Mr. Peroni said, looking at Tony's disappointed face. "Tony said he would take good care of Barney, and I'm going to hold him to his word."

Tony's head flew up. "You mean . . ."

"I mean we had better get Barney loaded before Mrs. Allen runs us out of here," Mr. Peroni said.

"Oh, boy!" Tony took hold of one end of the tank. Mr. Peroni took the other end, and they carried the heavy tank to the station wagon.

When they got home, Mr. Peroni and Tony carried Barney into the garage. Then Mr. Peroni went inside while Tony made Barney comfortable. A little later Tony's mother and father came out together.

Tony looked up happily. "Come and look, Mom. Barney's looking the place over."

Mrs. Peroni came a few steps farther and peered at the cage. Barney's tongue flickered as he moved closer to the glass. Mrs. Peroni took a quick step backward. "Beautiful, isn't he?" she said quietly. "What's he doing?"

"Just smelling you," Tony replied.

"He can smell me?" Mrs. Peroni gasped.

"Sure," Tony said. "He puts his tongue out to test the air, then puts it on the roof of his mouth. That's the way he smells."

"Smells!" Mrs. Peroni backed away. "I think I'll go check on my cake."

Tony watched her hurry back inside the house. "Don't you want to watch Barney climb up the tree branch?" he asked, disappointed.

Mr. Peroni smiled. "I guess your mother has had enough introduction to Barney for today."

"Oh," Tony said. "I forgot."

"Just don't forget to take good care of that snake. I don't want it getting loose and worrying your mother," Mr. Peroni warned.

"Oh, Barney can't get loose," Tony replied, giving the wire screen a little tap. "He is safe in here."

Barney stopped climbing and looked at Tony lazily.

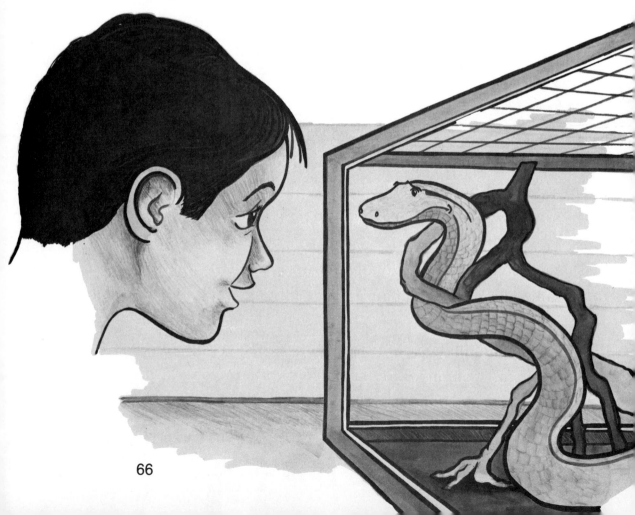

The next morning Tony was up before everyone else. His mother blinked when he opened the kitchen door. "Where have you been?" she asked, surprised.

"Out in the garage, checking on Barney," Tony replied, sniffing. "I smell pancakes!"

Mr. Peroni put his newspaper down as Tony slid into his seat at the table. Mr. Peroni winked at his wife. "First day of vacation and he didn't have to be called to come down. I wonder if we could borrow Barney for the school year."

"Aw, Dad." Tony grinned. "I just wanted to make sure nothing had bothered him during the night."

Mrs. Peroni looked at Tony in disbelief. "What would bother a three-foot snake?"

"A big dog, something like that," Tony replied seriously. "Dad, Mrs. Allen fed Barney yesterday, but he'll need something else before the week is over. Could I have three dollars?"

"Whoa now, Tony." Mr. Peroni shook his head. "You said you were going to take care of Barney yourself. That includes feeding him."

"Well, I guess I could catch some mice," Tony said thoughtfully.

"Mice? We don't have mice!" Mrs. Peroni set the juice down a little too hard. Tony wiped the spilled juice with a napkin.

"I know, Mom, but someone must have mice around here."

"What are you going to do, conduct a house-to-house survey?" Mr. Peroni chuckled.

Tony grinned. "I guess that wouldn't work. But all I need to get is two. I could raise the rest."

Mrs. Peroni shuddered. "What else do snakes eat?" she asked hastily.

"Birds, squirrels, things like that," Tony replied. "But Mrs. Allen always fed him white mice, just like the scientists do in laboratories."

Mrs. Peroni hesitated for a moment. Then she said slowly, "I wanted to do some painting and cleaning this summer, and the garage really needs to be cleaned out. I guess Tony could earn some extra money helping me."

"Thanks, Mom!" Tony beamed. "You're a lifesaver!"

Mr. Peroni grinned.

"What else could I say?" Mrs. Peroni smiled. "Live mice in the garage? I should hope not!"

Tony thought his problems were over, but he was wrong. Two weeks later Barney refused to eat his weekly meal.

Barney Goes to the Vet

Tony's mother was watching him try to coax Barney to eat when Mr. Peroni drove up after work. "Dad, Barney's sick," Tony called. "Come and look."

Mr. Peroni closed the car door and walked over to Barney's tank. "Maybe he isn't hungry," he said, tapping the glass. Barney didn't move.

"I don't know. He just doesn't look right," Tony said.

"Maybe he's getting ready to shed his skin," Mrs. Peroni suggested. "He's certainly grown a lot in two weeks!"

"If he were shedding his skin, his eyes would be milky," Tony said. "Look at them. They're clear as glass."

Mrs. Peroni glanced at Tony's worried face. "Would you feel better if your dad took him to the vet?"

"Oh, yes," Tony replied.

"Well, let's load his tank into the car," said Mr. Peroni.

Dr. Stewart took one look at Barney and knew exactly what was wrong with him. "Your pet has mites under his skin," he told them. "It's not serious now, but without proper care, he could die."

"What can I do?" Tony asked.

"First of all, clean his tank with ammonia. Then put all of Barney, except his nose, under lukewarm water for ten or fifteen minutes," said the vet. "Most of the mites should drown and fall off."

"Will he be cured after I give him his bath?" Tony asked.

"He'll need more than one bath to kill all the mites," said the vet. "You must give him two baths a day for the first two days. Then give him one bath a day for a week."

"Then will he be cured?" Tony asked.

"Not yet," said the vet. "Wait three or four days for the mite's eggs to hatch, then repeat the treatment. I'll give you a list of the medicines that you will need."

When Tony and his father got home, they explained Barney's problem to Mrs. Peroni. "In the tub? You want to give the snake a bath in my tub?"

"I'll use my bathroom, Mom," Tony explained. "And I'll take him right back to the garage. Please, Mom, I don't want him to die."

"Well, all right, but don't you bathe in that tub until that snake is well and the tub is scrubbed clean!"

"Fine, Mom, I don't get too dirty anyway," Tony said happily.

"That's not what I meant, young man!" Mom gave a helpless laugh. "You will use our bathroom."

"Aw," Tony said and left to get Barney. Mrs. Peroni disappeared into the kitchen and didn't come out until Barney was back in the garage.

Each day Tony washed Barney. When his bath was over, Tony carried him back to the garage. After the first few days Mrs. Peroni got used to seeing Barney looped over Tony's arm twice a day. One day Tony was surprised to see her in the doorway watching him bathe Barney.

"Doesn't he try to get loose?" she asked, staring at Barney's head firmly held in Tony's grasp.

"No, Barney's tame," Tony said, rubbing Barney's head with his free hand. "He sort of likes it."

Mrs. Peroni watched, fascinated. "How long does that thing actually grow?"

"Probably five or six feet," Tony answered. "They don't get too big."

"Six feet?" His mother shuddered. Then she asked with sudden suspicion, "How fast does he grow?"

"Aw, Mom, he's not going to get that long," Tony replied. "Not this summer, anyway. Mrs. Allen is going to give him to the zoo when he is four feet. He won't be grown then."

"Good!" Mrs. Peroni brightened. She even gave Barney a smile. Barney flickered his tongue as if in response.

"See, Mom," Tony said. "He likes you."

"Really?" Mrs. Peroni looked at the snake curiously. "I'm not sure I can say the same."

A few days later, Mrs. Peroni had a ladies' meeting at her house. She rushed around all day preparing for the meeting. Around a quarter to four she called Tony. "Have you given Barney his bath yet?"

"Not yet," he answered. "Why?"

"Why? Because I'm having a meeting at four today. Hurry up and get Barney out of the way!"

"Yes, ma'am!" Tony hurried to the garage to get Barney. He had Barney wrapped around his shoulders and had just reached the kitchen door when the first car drove up. Tony hurried inside and raced upstairs to the bathroom.

"Whew!" he said to Barney as he closed the door. "That was close!"

Soon Barney was floating happily in lukewarm water, his head safely in Tony's hand. Tony stroked his head and talked softly to him. It was after four when Barney was bathed and dried.

"Now how am I going to get you back downstairs?" Tony asked thoughtfully. "The ladies are all in the living room."

Barney coiled happily around the clothes hamper. "You aren't the easiest thing to hide," Tony added. He watched as Barney rubbed his head against the top of the wicker hamper.

"All right," Tony chuckled, opening the top of the hamper. "Get in!"

Barney slithered over the top of the hamper and disappeared into the clothes. Tony opened the door and peeked over the railing. The room was full of ladies. Tony sighed and went back to the bathroom. He sat for a while with his arms around his knees.

After a while he whispered, "Barney!" There was no sound from the hamper. "Barney must be taking a nap," he thought. He opened the hamper. Barney was coiled up in the clothes. Tony closed the lid and sat for a few more minutes. His eyes kept coming back to the hamper.

"I could take the hamper to the garage," he thought. "Barney is asleep and the hamper doesn't weigh much. Sure, it'll work."

Cheerfully he picked up the hamper and opened the door. Halfway down the stairs, he looked across the room and saw Mrs. Peroni's face. "It's Barney," Tony moved his mouth without actually speaking.

Mrs. Peroni nodded and stayed where she was. She watched every step Tony made. She looked rather like she was holding her breath.

Tony stepped off the last stair and started across the wooden floor. The hamper wasn't too heavy, but it was more awkward to carry than he had expected. He was doing fine, though, until Mrs. Perkins looked up and saw Mrs. Peroni's face.

"Anna!" she exclaimed. "Whatever is the matter?"

At that moment, Tony's foot came down on a scatter rug. The rug slipped and Tony sprawled on the floor. The hamper slid right into the middle of the living room.

"I'll get it! I'll get it!" Tony yelled as several ladies got up to help.

He was too late.

Three feet of shaken boa constrictor flowed from the overturned hamper and slithered across the floor.

Screams echoed in the room as ladies scrambled in all directions. Tony dashed after

Barney as he disappeared under the couch.

"It's only a boa constrictor," he heard his mother call to the excited ladies.

"Only a boa constrictor!" Mrs. Perkins's voice carried over the noise. "Anna, what are you thinking about, letting your child keep a boa constrictor in the house!"

"It's only a baby," Mrs. Peroni replied rather sharply. "It won't hurt you. Now calm down while I help Tony."

Most of the ladies gathered on the other side of the room, but a few came to help.

One knelt beside Tony and his mother. "It
doesn't squeeze, does it?"

"No, Barney's tame and anyway, he's been fed,"
Tony replied. "If you just chase him over here, I
can catch him."

Mrs. Peroni and some of the other ladies
carefully shooed Barney back to Tony's side of the
couch. Tony picked Barney up and wrapped him
around his arm. "There, didn't I tell you he was
tame?" Tony said proudly.

"And he belongs in the garage, not in the house," Mrs. Peroni said firmly. "Out, Tony!"

As Tony went out the door he could hear the ladies' excited comments.

"A boa constrictor! Anna, you're amazing!"

"They're fascinating! Did you know they can swallow an animal larger than their own heads?"

"Yes," Mrs. Peroni replied dryly, "I had noticed."

"But just imagine, keeping one in your house loose like that. Doesn't it make your skin crawl?"

"Well," Tony heard his mother say hesitantly, "you get used to it after a while. Barney isn't so bad. Why the other day . . . . "

Tony grinned and opened the back door. "You hear that, Barney?" he said to the boa constrictor. "You just might not have to stay in the garage all summer after all!"

The Legend of
WILLIAM TELL

Legends are very old stories that might possibly have happened. Some might be based on actual happenings; others might grow out of rumor or gossip. All, however, have changed or grown somewhat in the retelling. The following legend is about William Tell, a brave archer from the country of Switzerland. Long ago, the Emperor of Austria claimed Switzerland as his own and sent a man named Gessler to rule the land in his stead. Gessler was a cruel tyrant. One of his greatest pleasures was to see the proud Swiss acknowledge his power. In the marketplace he had placed a tall pole. On the top of the pole he placed his hat. This hat became a sign of his power, and Gessler insisted that every Swiss man, woman, or child who passed by the pole should bow to the hat. It is at this point that our story begins.

William Tell strode through the marketplace, his big bow and quiver strapped to his back. Peter almost had to run to keep up with him. Greetings rang out through the marketplace on every side as he and Peter passed. Peter beamed as he heard one man tell a stranger, "That's William Tell, the best archer in the country. Why one time I saw him split one arrow in flight with another from his quiver. And another time . . ."

Peter looked up at his tall father with pride. He thought how straight his father held himself, straight as a mountain pine, straight as Gessler's pole.

Peter pulled on his father's sleeve. "Father, the pole is still up there. The one with Gessler's hat on it, I mean."

"Yes, son, I see it." William Tell smiled down at Peter. "But we will not bow. We must not lose our courage, or we'll never be free again." William Tell began to walk faster. He passed by the large sign attached to the pole without glancing at it.

He knew that on the sign Gessler had written in big black letters, "Whosoever shall not bow to this hat shall thereby take his life into his hands."

The tall man and his son strode on, up the mountain to their home. But in the marketplace their passage had been noted by Gessler's spies. "They did not bow," the spies muttered, hurrying to the palace.

When Gessler heard the spies' story, he ordered, "Bring the great archer . . . No, wait; bring his son also!"

That same day soldiers appeared at the mountain home of William Tell. When they read the summons to Tell, his face turned pale. "Why should Peter go?"

The soldiers shrugged. "Gessler has ordered it."

Tell strapped on his bow and quiver. He and Peter were escorted down the mountain trail to a meadow where Gessler waited. News of the summons had spread through the town, and the townspeople had gathered in the meadow. They stood silently, watching and listening.

"William Tell," Gessler sneered. "I hear many stories about your skill with a bow and arrow. I hear that you can even shoot a hornet out of the air."

William Tell waited without speaking. Peter stood close by his side.

"I also hear that you refuse to bow to my hat!" Gessler's eyes turned to Peter. "You refuse, and your son . . . I hear that you love your only son dearly."

Tell put his hand lightly on Peter's shoulder. "What man would not love his son?" he replied quietly. "Peter is a good, obedient boy."

"I'm sure of that." Gessler's lips curled in a thin smile. "He follows your example well. Perhaps he can help." Gessler's eyes met William Tell's. "I wish to see your skills with a bow and an arrow," he said. "You will shoot an apple from your son's head . . . at one hundred paces! Do it, and you go free. Refuse and you both die!"

A murmur arose from the townspeople. A child! Even Gessler could not be that cruel! But the soldiers quickly silenced them. William Tell and his son stood alone before the tyrant.

"You are a wicked man, Gessler," Tell said quietly. "You will soon pay for your wickedness."

Two guards seized Peter, taking him with them as they stepped off the hundred paces. Peter looked back over his shoulder at his father and called, "You can do it, Father!"

The hundred paces were carefully counted; then Peter was turned to face his father. Peter reached for the apple and placed it on his head. He stood straight and tall, just as he had seen his father do so many times.

William Tell drew two arrows from his quiver. The crowd pressed in close behind the soldiers. Then everyone stood still, hardly daring to breathe.

Tell's hand trembled a little as he began to fit one of the arrows into his bow. This was no time for fear. His son's life depended on his skill. Then across the hundred paces, a voice rang out.

"I trust you, Father!"

The great archer lifted his bow. He took careful aim with a steady hand. He let the arrow fly. The arrow pierced the apple and sped beyond the boy.

A great shout rose from the people. Peter came running across the meadow, throwing himself into his father's arms. "I knew you could do it; I knew you could!" he cried.

"Your father was not so sure," snarled Gessler. "I see he took two arrows from his quiver when only one was needed!"

William Tell looked over his son's head and spoke in a cold voice. "The second arrow was for thee, tyrant, had I missed my first shot!"

84

"Seize him!" shrieked the angry ruler.

But the townspeople, who had pressed even closer, threw themselves upon the soldiers. William Tell drew the second arrow and shot Gessler through the heart. In the confusion that followed, he took his boy by the hand and fled. At a nearby lake he found a boat, rowed to the other shore, and escaped with his son into the mountains.

> *Some people say that when his boy was safe, William Tell returned to lead the Swiss people in their fight for freedom. In any case, the tyrant was dead, and it didn't take long for the brave Swiss people to regain their country and their freedom.*

Bringing in the Sheaves

Do you think about the words of the hymns you sing? Sometimes it is hard to understand what the words of a hymn really mean. "Bringing in the Sheaves" is a hymn that you may not understand.

Sheaves are bundles of grain. Before modern farm equipment was invented, farmers gathered ripe grain by cutting the plants and tying them into bundles. Those sheaves were gathered up and stored in barns until the farmers had time to thresh the grain.

Wheat is a grain that must be harvested with special care. It must be cut and gathered when it is perfectly ripe. The ripe grain can fall off very easily; and if rain comes at the time of harvest, the grain can spoil.

Farmers cannot control the time of ripeness or weather at harvest time. So a farmer was grateful when he was able to get all the crop cut, tied, and carried to the barn when the weather was good without losing any of the ripened grain.

You can understand now why a preacher or a songwriter would use the word *sheaves* to teach people about precious souls. Soulwinning is just like bringing in the sheaves at harvest time. Souls must be handled with care, and they must be saved in time.

The next time you sing "Bringing in the Sheaves," think about the farmer who brings in his precious harvest. Think about bringing precious souls to Jesus. Jesus tells us in Luke 10:2 to pray to the Lord of the harvest for workers to help with "bringing in the sheaves."

Sowing in the morning,
Sowing seeds of kindness,
Sowing in the noontide
And the dewy eve;
Waiting for the harvest,
And the time of reaping,
We shall come rejoicing,
Bringing in the sheaves.

BRINGING IN THE SHEAVES

KNOWLES SHAW

GEORGE A. MINOR

1. Sow - ing in the morn - ing, sow - ing seeds of kind - ness,
2. Sow - ing in the sun - shine, sow - ing in the shad - ows,
3. Go - ing forth with weep - ing, sow - ing for the Mas - ter,

Sow - ing in the noon - tide and the dew - y eve; Wait - ing for the har - vest,
Fear - ing nei - ther clouds nor win - ter's chill - ing breeze; By and by the har - vest
Tho' the loss sus - tained our spir - it of - ten grieves; When our weep - ing's o - ver,

and the time of reap - ing, We shall come re-joic - ing, bring - ing in the sheaves.
and the la - bor end - ed, We shall come re-joic - ing, bring - ing in the sheaves.
He will bid us wel - come, We shall come re-joic - ing, bring - ing in the sheaves.

CHORUS

Bring - ing in the sheaves, bring - ing in the sheaves, We shall come re - joic -
Bring - ing in the sheaves, bring - ing in the sheaves, We shall come re - joic -

1.
ing, bring - ing in the sheaves;

2.
ing, bring - ing in the sheaves.

SHEAVES

Tales of how families had to work together in difficult times are part of our American heritage. The story of Minnie Mae is based on a real American family. At the age of sixteen, Minnie Mae finds herself in charge of the house, the harvest, and five younger brothers.

"Lemonade time!" Minnie Mae called across the hay field to the little group of workers around the hay wagon.

Mr. Schwartz tossed a forkful of hay up to Jesse on the wagon. "Your sister sure knows when to show up with a drink. Let's take a rest."

Dorland gave his hay rake one more pull, turning over a neat pile of prickly hay. Then he dropped his hot rake handle and started across the field to the shade tree. Nothing would taste better than cold lemonade on such a hot

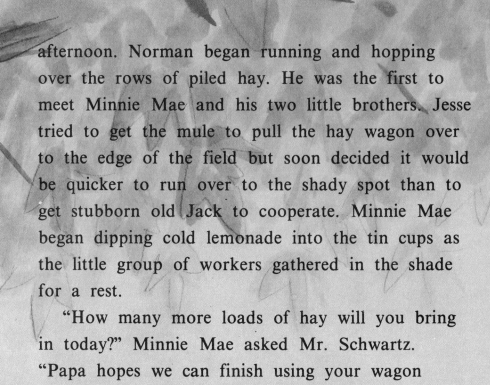

afternoon. Norman began running and hopping over the rows of piled hay. He was the first to meet Minnie Mae and his two little brothers. Jesse tried to get the mule to pull the hay wagon over to the edge of the field but soon decided it would be quicker to run over to the shady spot than to get stubborn old Jack to cooperate. Minnie Mae began dipping cold lemonade into the tin cups as the little group of workers gathered in the shade for a rest.

"How many more loads of hay will you bring in today?" Minnie Mae asked Mr. Schwartz. "Papa hopes we can finish using your wagon today."

"We'll make it by sundown if these three boys keep working like they've been doing." Mr. Schwartz wiped his big face with a red handkerchief. "It's hot, but it's a good day for bringing in the hay."

"We'll have to finish before sundown today, Mr. Schwartz," Minnie Mae said. "I have to get all these dirty boys cleaned up for church tomorrow. If Owen and Myrick can ride on the wagon, I can stay out and help until supper."

"Good. You can help Dorland with his row." Mr. Schwartz patted eight-year-old Dorland on the shoulder as he spoke.

Dorland held out his empty cup and smiled a quiet thank you as Minnie Mae dipped out a refill.

"How's your pa feeling today, Minnie Mae?" Mr. Schwartz held his cup for a refill too.

"He was up on the porch when I left, but this hot weather makes his cough worse," Minnie Mae replied as she began to gather the cups.

"Too bad. That leaves lots of work for you, Minnie Mae—lots of work for a sixteen-year-old girl." Mr. Schwartz lifted Owen to his shoulders for a ride across the field.

"I know Papa is thankful for your help, Mr. Schwartz," said Minnie Mae.

The cups clinked in the empty pail as the little group walked across the hot field. Myrick and Owen ran ahead, eager to climb on the hay wagon.

The harvesters were soon back at work, raking the hay and loading the wagon. Myrick and little Owen climbed higher and higher on the growing pile of hay. Squealing with laughter, they stomped it down to make room for Mr. Schwartz's big forkfuls. One time the dusty hay made Myrick sneeze so hard that he nearly came tumbling down the stack. Everyone laughed when little Owen pretended to sneeze too.

When the last load was ready, Dorland climbed up and sat happily beside Mr. Schwartz as he coaxed old Jack to pull the hay wagon up the barn hill. Minnie Mae and the two older boys followed with the rakes over their shoulders. They could have easily walked home faster than Jack with his load of children and hay, but there was something special about being right there when the last load of hay went into the barn.

Early the next morning Minnie Mae took the shiny milk pail out to the barn. Inside the door she stopped to take a deep breath. The tingly smell of fresh hay filled the barn.

"Hay smells so clean," thought Minnie Mae as she picked up the three-legged stool from the corner.

"We don't have any time to waste, Bessy," Minnie Mae whispered to the patient old cow. "You know what day it is." Patting the gentle beast, Minnie Mae settled down for milking. She guided her expert fingers while she listened to the soft "shoowee-shoowee" sound of the milk as it hit the pail. The smooth rhythm of the milking and the warm darkness of the barn sent Minnie Mae's thoughts out into the good open fields of the North Carolina farm that was her home.

Her thoughts drifted to yesterday's happy afternoon of bringing in the hay. She giggled at the thought of Myrick's big sneeze from the hay wagon. Then she remembered last year's haying team before Mama died . . .

"Minnie Mae." The barn door creaked open,
and a sleepy-eyed face appeared. It was Myrick,
half-dressed. "Minnie Mae, I can't find my socks."

"Myrick, you know better than to be out here
barefooted! I may have left your socks on the line
by mistake. I'll look for them, but get back
inside!" She watched as the little figure bobbed up
and down, heading back toward the house.

"Thank you for the milk, Bessy." She hastily
rubbed the old cow's nose. "You always seem to
give more on Sunday."

Minnie Mae poured the pail of milk into the
old crock and thought of how much she loved

Sundays. Her father was sick and her mother had died just before Easter. Her four older brothers were all away at school. So Minnie Mae had the care of all five of her little brothers. Sunday was a special time to show her love for them.

"Minnie Mae." A voice stopped her as she bent over the crock to carry it to the spring. It was Norman. "Minnie Mae, I can't find my tie."

"Why, Norman, I'm sure I saw it in your room somewhere. I'll be in with the milk in a few minutes. Hurry on!" She watched him as he turned obediently to the house.

"Bessy, I'll be late yet." Minnie Mae scooped up the milk crock and headed down the hill to the spring. "These brothers of mine," she said to a passing butterfly. Her voice had a scolding tone, but there was also a note of love and pride underneath it. They were all so different, and yet they were all so alike. They were all so . . .

She sighed as she set the crock down in the gurgling spring and picked up the crock from last night's milking. The rich cream had settled on top. "Bringing in the sheaves," she hummed under her breath as she trudged back up the hill. "Bringing in the sheaves." She would have five darling sheaves to bring in today, as she did almost every Sunday.

"Minnie Mae." That gentle voice belonged to Dorland, and Minnie Mae looked around with a smile. Dorland was the middle of the five little brothers. "Minnie Mae, do you know where my shoes are?" A shy smile spread over Dorland's handsome little face as if he knew that two of the other brothers had been out here already.

"Check under the beds, Dorland. And be sure to comb your hair carefully. Your cowlick is sticking up."

"I will, Minnie Mae. Can I help you with that?"

"No, but if you'll gather the eggs, that will help." Minnie Mae smiled as Dorland raced away. "How much trouble little brothers seem to have in getting ready to go to church!" she thought. "And here comes Owen! A two-year-old needs help finding everything!"

In the next little while Minnie Mae scrambled the eggs, fried the sausages, skimmed the milk, dressed Owen, scrubbed Myrick's face, and helped all her brothers find their missing clothes.

Before she dressed for church, Minnie Mae ran out to the barn to hitch Jack to the buggy. "You stubborn old mule," she chided him. "You had better remember what day it is and hurry up." Jack snorted in her face.

"Come on, get up there!" she said as she pulled at the bridle. Finally Jack shook his head and let himself be pulled into the yard and hitched up. She patted him on his neck and then ran back inside.

"Everybody about ready to go?"

A flurry of answers responded to her call. "I am." "Almost." "Minnie Mae, come help me." "Jesse, stop that."

Minnie Mae sighed and hurried to help them.
"Now I mustn't forget to dress myself, you know,"
she said. She glanced down at the old dress she
wore and grinned. "What a sight I'd be if I went
to church looking like this!"

She carefully took out her beautiful navy blue
Sunday dress. It had buttons down the front,
sparkly black buttons. It was her pride and joy.

Then came her high-button shoes. Even though
she put them on as quickly as she could, she still
took a long time in doing so. Those high-button
shoes were lovely things to wear, but they
certainly were a lot of trouble. She put in the
hairpins that had fallen out of her thick brown

hair. She made sure it was neatly piled on her head before she put on her best Sunday hat.

Finally at ten o'clock, all six of the children were ready to go. Each little boy in turn kissed Papa and scrambled outside. Minnie Mae kissed him last. Dear Papa. She could remember when Mama and Papa liked nothing better than going to church and sitting with their family for the singing and preaching. Papa squeezed Minnie Mae's hand, and his blue eyes twinkled at her. She loved him so.

"Minnie Mae, come on! We'll be late!" Five heads of varying sizes stuck themselves back inside the door.

"Get on out into the buggy. Shoo!" Minnie Mae knew they wouldn't be late as long as Jack cooperated.

She climbed into the buggy and took the reins. She asked as she did every Sunday, "Do you all have your Bibles?" As often as not one of them forgot his. But this time she was greeted with a chorus of "Yes!"

"Get up, Jack, get up!" Minnie Mae called to the old mule, snapping the reins. It almost always took Jack a few minutes to decide to go, and today he seemed to feel especially ornery. "You stubborn old mule," Minnie Mae murmured. She snapped the reins and called again. "Get up there!" Jack finally took off with a jerk.

"Here we go, off to church," she thought. Minnie Mae's heart sprang up inside her. All her precious little brothers were going to church with her. It was something she never tired of.

"Let's sing," Minnie Mae said. And they sang to the rhythm of Jack's hooves clopping on the dirt road. "Bringing in the sheaves, bringing in the sheaves, we shall come rejoicing, bringing in the sheaves."

At church Minnie Mae met her friend Elizabeth, the pastor's daughter. They exchanged a few quick words and giggles before walking into church. But Minnie Mae made sure that all five little brothers were close by.

Mr. Schwartz, the usher at the door, certainly looked different in his Sunday clothes. "Good morning, Minnie Mae," he said. "I see you managed to get the hay out of all this straw-colored hair."

Minnie Mae smiled as she led the boys to a wooden pew near the front of the church. There they sat, seven in a row. Minnie Mae sat by Elizabeth, but she looked down the row of little brothers. She saw the studious, quiet faces and prayed, "Lord, let each of them come to know You when the time is right."

The congregation sang. The choir sang. And there in that little church, the preacher preached a Bible message. Minnie Mae heard a sniff. She looked down the row of brothers to see tears running down Dorland's cheeks.

When the congregation stood to sing "Jesus, I Come," Dorland left his seat in the old wooden pew and walked to the front of the church.

After church when everyone was outside, Dorland slipped up to his big sister. "Minnie Mae, do you know what I did this morning?" he asked softly.

"Please tell me, Dorland." Her words were gentle but eager.

"I asked Jesus into my heart."

Minnie Mae hugged Dorland tightly. He said, "The preacher was talking about sin, and all of a sudden I knew that I was a sinner."

She nodded. Even children who are sweet, just naturally sweet, even they need to be saved, she thought. But she said, "Mama would have been glad, Dorland. You must tell Papa when we get home. He'll want to know."

Dorland nodded.

"Now run and climb into the buggy. I'm bringing Elizabeth home for dinner." Dorland ran to the buggy where the other brothers were already gathering.

Before long Minnie Mae and Elizabeth were there too. Minnie Mae unhitched Jack from the post. He snorted and tossed his head. "Steady there, Jack," Minnie Mae said. "I know you've been waiting a long time. Steady."

Minnie Mae climbed up next to Elizabeth. All five brothers sat in the back. Minnie Mae snapped the reins and called, "Get up there, Jack! Get up there!" Jack didn't move. "Get up, Jack!" Jack snorted and tossed his head. Suddenly he moved forward. "No, this way." Minnie Mae jerked the reins to the right. Jack jerked to the left and bucked. Suddenly the buggy was over on its side.

Owen let out a howl. People came running from the church to see if anyone had been hurt. Elizabeth's father, Pastor Reese, ran out too. His long coattails flew out behind him. "Children, children, are you all right?"

Mr. Schwartz grabbed Jack's reins and calmed the mule down. Minnie Mae crawled out of the buggy. Pastor Reese helped the others climb out and held Owen in his arms. Elizabeth brushed off her dress and began to laugh. Soon everyone was laughing and talking as the men turned the buggy right side up.

At home Papa sighed with relief when he heard the end of the story of the overturned buggy. All through dinner the main topic of conversation was Jack. "He's ornery, all right." "Just plain stubborn, that's all. When he makes up his mind to do something, there's no changing it." Only Dorland was quiet. Minnie Mae saw him playing with his food and looking uncomfortable. Minnie Mae knew what Dorland wanted to say, but somehow the time never seemed right for him.

Dinner ended and the kitchen was cleaned up. If the weather was good, Sunday was the day for an afternoon walk. Minnie Mae liked to go walking with all five of her brothers, but today she begged Elizabeth to take four of them. Today she wanted to walk with no one but Dorland.

The two sets of footsteps crackled the sticks and crunched the leaves that were beginning to fall. Minnie Mae and Dorland didn't talk for a while. They walked by the garden where pumpkins and tall corn waited for the harvest. They passed the shorn hayfield and made their way up the hill. Sunlight warmed them through the thinning yellow leaves of the birch trees. Minnie Mae put her hand in Dorland's hand.

"You didn't tell Papa that you were saved today, Dorland," she said.

"No, I didn't." His face was sober.

"Was it because of all the commotion about Jack and the buggy?"

Dorland nodded and looked away.

Minnie Mae brushed off an old log and sat down with Dorland beside her. "You know he'll be happy to find out. You can tell him just the way you told me."

There was silence for a moment.

Then Dorland smiled at Minnie Mae. "You're right," he said. Hand in hand they tramped back down the hill toward the house. Minnie Mae was singing softly as they walked by the newly cut hay field.

> "Bringing in the sheaves,
> bringing in the sheaves,
> We shall come rejoicing,
> bringing in the sheaves . . . ."

Diary of a Pilgrim Boy

We have learned much about history from the men, women, and children who kept journals. In these journals they recorded events of daily life that tell us how they lived, and events of importance that tell us what happened during the time they lived. William Bradford's journal records the struggles of the colonists as they began their life in a new land. The story of Love's diary is historical fiction although it is based on true events.

On September 6, 1620, the *Mayflower* sailed away from Plymouth, England. One hundred two men, women, and children from Holland and England were crowded onto the deck, looking back at the Old World one last time.

Nine-year-old Love Brewster stood at the railing beside his father, mother, and younger brother. He watched the coast of England grow smaller and smaller. Love missed his older brother and sisters. When he thought of the wild animals, the Indians, and the cold winters in America, he longed for his home in Holland.

William Bradford, one of Elder Brewster's friends, patted Love's shoulder. "We are pilgrims on this earth," he said. "Our eyes should be on our heavenly home."

Love's father smiled. "We may worship God as we choose in the new land," he said. "We must have courage, and trust in God's strength."

Love watched as William Bradford took out his journal and moved away to find a good place to write. "I'll keep a journal like Master Bradford is doing," Love decided. "Then I'll have a record of our voyage also."

September 6, 1620

Today we sailed from Plymouth. We left our smaller ship, the *Speedwell*, behind. The men did not think the *Speedwell* could make the long ocean voyage.

Our ship is loaded with food. There are barrels of salted beef, pork, and fish. There are also boxes of smoked fish and dried ox tongues, and bushels and bushels of vegetables and flour. We even have butter and pickled eggs!

Mother says we will need all of this food. It must last until our first harvest next year.

We are taking many other goods to our new home. Mother packed our clothes, blankets, rugs, pots, pans, lanterns, knives, and spoons. Father brought his books, tools, guns, and armor.

Some of the passengers from England brought extra supplies. One of the merchants brought 126 pairs of shoes and 13 pairs of boots. Others brought copper chains, beads, and mirrors to trade with the Indians.

Father says that our people and the passengers who are strangers to us must work together. He says it takes many different kinds of workers to start a new colony.

September 7, 1620

Our ship's captain, Master Jones, gave his cabin to the women, girls, and babies. Father and I slept with the other men down on the gun deck.

Last night I could not sleep. The gun deck smelled like fish and tar. The ship's cat chased rats across the crowded floor.

This morning my friend, Bartholomew, and I climbed to the upper deck. The fresh salt air smelled good. We stood at the front of the ship and pretended we were on a warship. I was the captain.

September 8, 1620

Today Bartholomew and I sneaked into the sailors' cook room. We tasted the sweet raisin pudding simmering on the brick stove.

The cook roared angrily when he saw us. Sleepy sailors who had worked all night were startled by the cook's loud roar. They jumped out of their hammocks and chased us away.

September 9, 1620

This morning Bartholomew and I escaped from his two little sisters and my brother. We watched the sailors wash the deck and mend the sails. We watched them climb like spiders up the ship's masts and turn the sails to catch the wind.

Bartholomew and I climbed up to the half-deck at the back of the ship. We watched Master Jones lift a stick to the sun and make marks on his map.

In the afternoon one of the mates allowed us to keep time. I sat by the half-hour glass and Bartholomew sat by the bell. When the sand ran through the glass, I turned it over while Bartholomew rang the bell. We were very careful. We wanted to keep the correct time.

Later we took off our shoes and stockings and began climbing the masts. Our mothers scolded us and sent us below. "You must not bother the sailors," they said. "Besides, you might hurt yourselves."

September 11, 1620

Yesterday was Sunday. The members of the church gathered together on the upper deck. Some of the passengers from England joined our worship service. The sailors just laughed and turned away.

Our service was much shorter than usual. We sang a psalm and Father prayed. Then he read Hebrews 11 and talked about having faith in God.

In the afternoon Father taught my friends and me. He helped us read the Bible. He also asked us our catechism questions.

September 13, 1620

Many of our people are very ill. Now Father thinks that the ship's rocking motion has given us sick stomachs. Our doctor agrees with him.

One of the sailors wants us to die. He curses us every day. "I hope to throw half of you overboard before the journey's end," he says. "I will enjoy your supplies."

Mother says that God will punish any man that curses His people.

September 14, 1620

I could not eat my cheese and biscuit today. I think that I am getting ill.

September 23, 1620

Today I ate a little supper for the first time in a week. I am glad to be over my seasickness.

While I was sick, God struck the ungodly sailor with a terrible sickness. He died and was thrown overboard. The sailors have been kinder to us since then.

God kept us safe through our sickness and delivered us from this evil man. Mother and Father were right. God does take care of us.

September 29, 1620

Father and the other men are learning to shoot their muskets. Captain Standish says they must be prepared to hunt wild animals and defend themselves against the Indians.

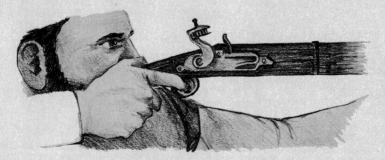

Our captain is a real soldier. He makes the men load their guns again and again. If they make a mistake, his face turns as red as his hair.

When the men pull their triggers, I hold my ears. Then I hold my nose! The blast fills the air with black smoke and the smell of rotten eggs.

Sometimes a man will fall over when he fires his musket. "Try once more," says Captain Standish. "You must not let your musket kick against you."

Once Father let me hold his musket. It is longer than I am, and I could not hold it steady. Captain Standish told me not to worry. He will teach me to shoot when I get older.

October 4, 1620

This morning the sky was dark and stormy. All day the waves have grown rougher. Bartholomew and I ran back and forth along the deck, dodging the salt-water spray. Master Jones says we are in for some bad weather.

November 4, 1620

I hope the storms have ended. I have never been so wet, so hungry, and so afraid. We were tossed back and forth on the dark, crowded gun deck while rain and seawater poured through the cracks. Many times I thought we were going to sink. It was so dark and cold that I couldn't write in my diary.

When the storms began many weeks ago, huge waves broke over the deck. The sailors pulled up their hoods, climbed the ship's masts, and rolled down the sails. Master Jones made us all go down into the gun deck. The sailors tied themselves to the ship's rails and stayed on duty during the storms. The sailor's life lines kept them from falling overboard when giant waves washed over the upper deck.

Father wondered if the hard winds were blowing us off course. Mother was afraid that the ship might sink. Every day I prayed to God with all my heart.

Now that the storms are over, Father says that we must hold a special worship service. We will praise God for all His blessings during the storms.

November 7, 1620

Today we had our special service. Father reminded us about all the blessings during the storms.

One day the ship's main beam cracked and water poured into the gun deck. Some of the sailors wanted to turn back, but Master Jones knew our ship was strong. Father and the other men unpacked a great iron screw. They used it to push the beam back into place.

On another day Goodman John Howland climbed to the upper deck during a storm. Without warning the ship rolled, and he fell into the ocean. As he fell, Goodman Howland grabbed a hanging rope. The sailors pulled him back with a boat hook.

God also cared for Mistress Hopkins during the storms. He gave her a healthy baby boy named Oceanus. Master Hopkins said the baby's name will remind us of God's care while we sailed across the ocean.

And Father says we are still on course! The storms didn't blow us off course, and we'll be looking for land every day now. We sang praises to God. Bartholomew and I sang louder than anyone else on the ship.

November 8, 1620

The skies are blue every day now. Bartholomew and I are the first ones on deck in the morning. We want to be the first to see land.

November 10, 1620

The sailors say we are very close to land now. Bartholomew and I wanted to sleep on deck tonight, but Master Jones said no.

November 11, 1620

I woke up before dawn this morning. I could hear the sailors up on the deck. I sat up and listened until I could stand it no longer. Crawling over to Bartholomew, I found him awake too. We climbed the ladder to the deck. Master Jones let us stand with him.

High up in the rigging a sailor shouted, "Land!" We ran to the railing. I could hear the others rushing to the deck. Land in the distance! Thank you, God! Thank you for bringing us safely across the ocean to our new home!

Toys from Nature

Just suppose that you are all alone in a meadow. It is a beautiful day in early summer. The birds are singing. Daisies and clover are swaying in the gentle breeze.

Now pretend that you must spend the whole day in this meadow. You do not have any toys. How would you spend the day? What would you do? Would you miss your friends, books, and toys?

Pioneer children did not have a hard time filling their days. They often worked from sunrise to sunset with their parents.

But when these children had some free time, they often played in the woods and meadows, making many of their own games and toys. With a little work and imagination, they turned ordinary objects of nature into treasured playthings.

The children often built playhouses by piling pine needles into the rough shapes of chests, tables, and beds. When their make-believe houses were finished, the girls pretended to cook, sew, and care for their special dolls that they made from grass and twigs. Apples, pears, turnips, potatoes, nuts, and even daisies were sometimes used for dolls' heads. After using corncobs and cornstalks to make other dolls, the girls would twist corn silk into yellow braids for dolls' hair.

The dolls were not finished until the girls had dressed them. In the girls' hands, dried cornhusks tied with corn silk became lovely dresses. Leaves of all shapes and sizes became aprons, hats, and sunshades. Tiny daisy chains and seed necklaces completed the dolls' outfits.

When the dolls were dressed, the girls built doll-houses. Sometimes they made "log cabins" with corncobs. At other times they just cleared the dirt away from big tree roots to form "dugouts."

Of course, each dollhouse needed furniture. By sticking burrs together, the girls made tables, chairs, and beds. They built cradles from corn-husks and milkweed pods. Tiny pine needles made perfect brooms. They even made acorn bowls, rose-hip teacups, and birch-bark drinking cups.

The dolls' tables looked bare without food, so the girls gathered berries and seeds. Pulling off daisy petals, the girls used the flowers' centers as "pumpkin pies." Then they made thick mud pies and weak mud tea.

Pioneer boys also played with objects from the meadows and woods. They played games and built toys that improved their skills in fishing, hunting, tracking, and fighting.

Some of these toys were simple to make. By tying a vine to a tree branch or a cane stalk, the boys had a fishing pole. In their eyes, a large stick became a snorting horse.

The boys often used simple toys to improve their aim. They made flat stones skip and slide over the surface of rivers or streams. Hard, round berries served as marbles. Pointing certain flowers, like the touch-me-nots, at targets, the boys popped the seeds. They threw darts made from half a corncob and four chicken feathers, and they carried long cornstalk "spears" as they followed wild animal tracks on their stick horses.

Toys from Nature   123

Other games and toys were harder to make. Using their pocketknives, the boys hollowed out elder and willow branches to make beanshooters or blowpipes.

The boys also made noisemakers with their knives. From dandelion stems they formed horns, and from weeping willow branches they cut willow whistles. They also carved flat wooden paddles, called "bull-roarers." When the boys tied these bull-roarers to strings and swung them around and around, the flat paddles sounded like angry, snorting bulls.

Down by the stream the boys built twig-and-leaf "flutter mills" that turned like windmills as the flowing water lifted each leaf.

Pioneer boys and girls played with all of these games and toys—and many more. They filled their playtimes with activity because their imaginations never stopped working.

Just suppose that you are still alone in a meadow. Now how would you spend the day? Could you think of more things to do?

The Secret Pony

(historical fiction)

The Stahl family left their home in Germany in 1741 and sailed for America. They purchased land outside Philadelphia and began to build a farm. Within the year a sturdy house and barn stood on the land. Then the family turned their attention to building fences and farming. For the youngest son, the fences couldn't be built fast enough.

A Lost Pony

The sun was shining and the birds were singing, but ten-year-old Jacob Stahl hardly noticed the beauty around him. It was market day and his brothers, Ernst and Hans, were loading the wagon. Jacob listened to their chatter as he herded the family's cows from the huge red barn.

"Nothing ever happens to me," Jacob grumbled to himself as the last cow left the barn. "Milk the cows. Take them to pasture. Bring them home before supper. Milk them again . . . my days never change."

Jacob grumbled all the way to the pasture. The herd of cows spread out across the green grass, the bells around their necks clanging as they lowered their noses and began grazing. Jacob plopped down into the sweet-smelling clover.

"I can't wait until the fences are done," he said to the cows. "Then you will be put in the pasture, and I can do something besides sit here all day."

Jacob forgot about the bull-roarer he had made yesterday and the fluttermill that still whirled down in the stream. He forgot about the cave he had found and kept for his secret place. All he could think about was that he couldn't go to market with his brothers.

Suddenly Jacob sat up. A tiny, reddish-brown pony with a coal-black mane and tail was galloping toward him!

Jacob whistled. "She's beautiful!" he said out loud.

At the sound of Jacob's whistle, the pony stopped in her tracks and stared at the boy. Then she arched her neck, shook her head, and galloped off.

Jacob held his breath while the pony swerved in and out among the cows. The cows just flicked their tails and kept eating.

"Where did she come from?" Jacob wondered as the pony rolled over and over in the soft grass.

Each time Jacob tried to get near the pony, she snorted, laid her ears back, and galloped away. At last Jacob sat quietly and watched her graze beside the cows.

"I'll catch you on the morrow," he promised. "Won't everyone be surprised when I come home leading a pony!"

The next morning Jacob was dressed five minutes before his mother called him. He beat Ernst downstairs and helped Hans milk the cows. Then he gobbled down his breakfast.

"Why are you in such a hurry?" asked his father in German.

"It's spring!" said Jacob. He drank the last drop of creamy milk, leaving a white mustache on his upper lip.

"I want to go to the pasture with Jacob," said nine-year-old Abigail.

Jacob sighed with relief when his mother shook her head.

"We must clean the house," Frau Stahl reminded her daughter. She turned to Jacob and added, "Wipe your mouth, son."

Jacob rubbed the back of his hand across his mouth. He grabbed a hunk of bread, some cheese, and an apple. Then he put on his hat and ran to the barn.

As he walked behind the cows a few minutes later, Jacob thought of just the right name for the pony.

"Molasses!" said Jacob, thinking of his mother's thick, reddish-brown molasses. "That's what I'll call her—Molasses!"

Jacob made sure that the cows were settled into the lower pasture before he searched for the pony. He held the apple in his left hand and dangled a rope from his other hand.

"Molasses! Oh, Molasses! Where are you?" he called.

A soft whinny came from the creek.

Jacob hummed as he walked very slowly toward the creek. He stopped at the edge of the water and held out the apple.

"Come on, girl. Here's your breakfast," said Jacob.

Molasses sniffed the apple, and then opened her mouth. Carefully Jacob moved his right hand toward the pony's shoulder.

"Come a little closer, Molasses," he said.

The pony took a few steps forward and snatched the apple from Jacob's hand. While she chewed, Jacob rubbed her forehead and patted her neck.

"That's a good girl," he said. He was still patting Molasses when he noticed the brand on her left shoulder and flank.

"Who is *IW*?" he wondered. "I don't know anyone with those initials."

Molasses just nuzzled Jacob's face.

"Well, I'll find out who you belong to later," Jacob decided as he slipped the rope over the pony's head. "Let's get out of this creek."

Molasses snorted and shook her head. She pulled hard against the rope as she backed into the water.

"Now, don't be stubborn," said Jacob. He followed the pony into the creek.

Jacob braced himself and pulled with all his might. Without warning, Molasses gave up. Jacob tumbled into the water. Molasses grabbed Jacob's hat in her teeth and galloped away.

Jacob's Secret

That night Jacob still didn't tell his family about the pony. He thought about looking in the newspaper his father had brought home from the market. Perhaps there was something about a missing pony. Jacob picked up the paper then put it down without reading it.

"I wish Molasses *could* be mine," he thought to himself. Somehow, after he had named the pony, it seemed more like his own.

The next morning, as soon as the cows were munching the thick green grass, Jacob searched for the pony. He found her near his secret cave. It was then the thought came to him.

"Maybe I wouldn't have to give you up right away," he said, peering into the cave. "This is the perfect hiding place. Molasses, you can be my secret for a little while!"

All afternoon, as the cows grazed nearby, Jacob piled rocks and tree branches in front of the cave.

He left a gap just wide enough for Molasses to walk in and out of her "home."

"When I cover this hole with a small bush, you'll be safe," said Jacob as he tied the pony inside the cave. "Nothing can hurt you in here."

Molasses pricked up her ears at the sound of Jacob's voice then rested her head on his shoulder. "This is a fine home," she seemed to say.

As the days passed, Jacob and Molasses became good friends. As soon as the cows were in the pasture, Jacob ran to untie Molasses.

Molasses always felt frisky after spending the night in the dark cave. When Jacob turned her loose outside, she charged toward him, not stopping until the last second.

When Jacob called, she pricked up her ears and galloped to him. She especially loved to sniff out the carrots and apples Jacob saved for her.

Sometimes when Jacob was sitting on her back, she would suddenly make a right-hand turn. Each time she pulled this trick, Jacob sailed straight through the air and landed with a "thud" on the hard earth.

"You know that trick too well," Jacob groaned, picking himself up for the umpteenth time. Then he thought guiltily, "I wonder how many times you tried that on your real owner?" Jacob pushed the thought out of his mind as he and Molasses followed the cows.

Jacob never stayed angry with Molasses, not even when she plopped down in the creek just after he had brushed her with an old comb.

As the days grew warmer, Molasses often stretched out in the pasture. When Jacob first saw the pony lying on her right side with her eyes closed, he thought she was dead. Then he saw the "dead" pony swat a fly with her tail.

"Don't frighten me like that," Jacob scolded.

Molasses just lifted her head and seemed to
say, "Why don't you join me?"

"I can't keep Molasses hidden forever," Jacob
thought. "Soon I'll have to tell my father. Then
he will look for the owner."

Even though he didn't want to lose Molasses,
Jacob worried about Molasses's owner. How old
was he? Was he searching for his pony?

The Decision

One day, Jacob thought of a plan that might help him keep the pony.

"Molasses may not have an owner any more," he said to himself. "I will read the advertisements in the newspaper. If no one places an advertisement for my pony, maybe Father will let me keep her."

A few days later Jacob eagerly waited for his father to return from the market in Philadelphia.

"Did you bring the *Gazette*?" he asked as soon as his father stepped down from the wagon.

"It's in the back," Herr Stahl replied. "I thought you didn't like to practice your English."

"I'm getting better every week," said Jacob. "I can understand most of the words."

"Well, help me unload the wagon," said his father. "You can read the newspaper after our Bible study."

As soon as the Bible study was over, Jacob reached for the newspaper. Quickly he turned to the advertisements. There was nothing about Molasses!

Each week when his father brought the paper home from the market, Jacob was the first to ask for it. Sometimes there was an advertisement for a lost horse. Jacob always held his breath until he was sure that the advertisement had been written about some horse other than Molasses.

Then one day Jacob's hopes were shattered. His heart seemed to stop as he read the following words:

> 17 June 1742: Strayed, about two months ago, from the Northern Liberties of this city, a small bay mare branded *IW*. . . . She, being but little and bare-footed, cannot be supposed to have gone far; therefore, if any of the town boys find her and bring her to the subscriber, they shall, for their trouble, have liberty to ride her when they please. William Franklin.

Jacob gasped when he read the name of Molasses's owner. William Franklin was Benjamin Franklin's eleven-year-old son!

Slowly Jacob put the paper down on the table. His father looked up. "Why, Jacob," he said, "what is the matter?"

"Molasses," he choked and ran outside.

Herr Stahl followed him. He found Jacob sitting on the steps, crying. He sat down beside the boy and waited. At last Jacob raised his head.

"The pony in the advertisement is Molasses," he said.

"Molasses?" asked his father.

"Yes," replied Jacob. "I found a pony and hid her in a cave."

For a moment Herr Stahl didn't speak. Then he said quietly, "You had better tell me all of it."

Jacob told his story haltingly, trying not to think of Molasses waiting by the creek, Molasses running in the sunshine, Molasses tucked safely into the secret cave.

When Jacob finished, Herr Stahl shook his head sadly. "You have done wrong, son," he said. "The pony was not yours to keep."

Jacob hung his head. "I know," he replied. "I'm sorry, Father. I wanted her so badly . . ." He stopped, and then looked at his father. "I want to return her myself, Father."

Herr Stahl nodded. "Yes. Next market day, we will take the pony to Mr. Franklin. In the meantime, bring the pony up to the barn. You must take good care of her."

"Yes, sir." As Jacob started to get up, his father spoke again.

"Jacob, your job is to take care of the cows. You will not be allowed to play with the pony again, only take care of her."

"I understand, Father." Jacob walked away slowly.

On the next market day the Stahls' wagon jolted down the narrow, bumpy road into Philadelphia. Molasses trotted happily at the end of her rope, but Jacob did not smile at the sight of her tossing head.

"What will Mr. Franklin say to me?" he wondered.

When the wagon stopped in front of the house and shop on Market Street, Molasses pawed the ground. She was glad to be home.

"I'll wait for you here," said Herr Stahl as Jacob climbed down from the wagon.

At that moment the shop door opened, and a large man with a cheerful face stepped outside.

Jacob swallowed. "Mr. Franklin," he called. The man turned around. "I found your son's pony, sir," he stammered.

Ben Franklin followed him to the back of the wagon. "Well, so you have," he said, patting the pony. "It is Lady Anne! You've taken good care of her. I will keep my promise. You may ride her whenever you come to town."

Jacob looked at Molasses longingly. Then he shook his head. "I'm sorry, sir. I hid your son's pony because I wanted to keep her. I don't deserve a reward."

Mr. Franklin looked at Jacob kindly. "I won't try to change your mind, but I do understand how much a boy can want a pony. William's not much older than you are. He'll be glad to get Lady Anne back."

Jacob swallowed and nodded. He turned to climb back into the wagon.

"Jacob," called Mr. Franklin, "stop in to see William next market day. I won't try to change your mind, but William might!"

Herr Stahl waved to Mr. Franklin and clucked to the horses. The wagon lurched forward as Mr. Franklin led Molasses around the corner of the printing shop. Jacob turned to his father.

The Secret Pony   139

"Do you think . . . ," he began hesitantly, then stopped.

His father gave Jacob a thoughtful look. "You know, Jacob," he said, "Mr. Franklin was right. You did take good care of Molasses. And you take good care of the cows. You took care of them even when you were playing with Molasses."

Jacob looked puzzled. "That was my job, Father."

"And sometimes you didn't like your job."

"Sometimes," Jacob replied. "I guess I got tired of the same thing every day."

"But you still did your job well," Herr Stahl said. "And I think you have learned not to keep someone else's property, haven't you?"

"Yes, sir."

"The fences are up, and next week we will put the cows into the fenced pasture. We will find something else for you to do, Jacob." Herr Stahl smiled at Jacob. "And from now on, you go to market with the other boys. Would you like that?"

"Yes, sir!" Jacob replied happily. A new job and market day! And maybe someday . . . maybe he could visit, just visit, William and Molasses.

Phillis Wheatley:

Slave Girl of Old Boston

In the summer of 1761 Susannah Wheatley was looking for a new slave to train to be her companion. On the slave block of Boston she found a small, seven-year-old Negro girl. The child was dressed only in the tattered remnants of a carpet. She was sick too, possibly as a result of the long ocean voyage on the slave ship. Other slave buyers passed her over because of her condition, but Mrs. Wheatley saw something she liked in the child's face. Having paid the slaver's price, she took the child to the Wheatley home on King Street and put her to bed.

The Wheatley twins entered the sickroom quietly. Eighteen-year-old Mary pulled up a chair next to the bed. Nathaniel stood beside a bedpost and looked over at his mother, who sat on the other side of the bed.

"How is she?" he whispered.

"She is better," Mrs. Wheatley replied, "although she coughs often. It will take her a while to get her strength back, even with medicine."

"She's a pretty little thing," Mary said, looking at the dark face against the pillow. "What are you going to call her?"

"Phillis," Mrs. Wheatley replied. "Phillis Wheatley. It's a good name and it suits her. Let's let her rest now."

As the days went by, the rest and the medicine did their work. Phillis grew stronger every day. When she was up and about, she found that she was the youngest member of the Wheatley household. Phillis responded to the family's kindness with affection. Mrs. Wheatley, surprised at how quickly Phillis learned to speak English, asked Mary to become Phillis's teacher. Mary began to give Phillis reading lessons, and in sixteen months Phillis was reading difficult passages in the Bible.

One day Mrs. Wheatley found Phillis trying to write on the wall with a piece of charcoal.

"Has Mary taught you to write?" Mrs. Wheatley asked in astonishment.

"No, ma'am," Phillis answered. "When I think

of words that I have read in the Bible, I want to write them down so I won't forget them."

"We'll have to teach you to write," said the amazed Mrs. Wheatley. "Mary will get you some paper and a pen."

Phillis did learn to write, and went on to study Latin and the classics when she was twelve. She loved poetry and liked to write her own poems.

"Someday I would like to write poems like this one," she told Mrs. Wheatley, showing her a favorite poem in a book of poetry.

"I wouldn't be surprised if you do, Phillis," her mistress replied, shaking her head in amusement. "You do amaze me, child."

Realizing that Phillis had special abilities, the Wheatleys required only light housework from her, allowing her to continue her studies.

During the year that Phillis turned twelve the Stamp Act was repealed. The repeal of the tax that had been so despised by all the colonies was a reason for rejoicing and celebrating.

Phillis could scarcely control her excitement. Running from window to window, she watched the colored ribbons fluttering in the branches of the trees.

They're beautiful!" she exclaimed, turning to Mrs. Wheatley. "When do the fireworks begin?"

"You'll have to wait until nightfall," Mrs. Wheatley said, smiling at the eager girl. "Run and help Mary put candles in all the windows. Tonight we'll celebrate the repeal of the Stamp Act."

Phillis hurried to obey. By the time she and Mary had finished, it was getting dark outside. "It's time we left," Mr. Wheatley said. "There will be a crowd on Boston Common tonight."

The family and Phillis rode in the Wheatley carriage to Boston Common. They joined the crowd and waited for the fireworks to begin. Phillis gasped in delight when rockets shot into the sky and pinwheels scattered sparks in every direction on the ground.

"It's wonderful," she said to her mistress. "I'll write a poem to tell King George so!"

When she got home, Phillis lit a candle and picked up her quill pen. She wrote her first poem, thanking King George for repealing the Stamp Act. Mrs. Wheatley was pleased with the poem and encouraged Phillis to write more. Phillis liked to write about events that happened in the city or at home.

One day she heard two visitors at the Wheatley home talking about a narrow escape from an accident at sea.

"Where would those men have gone if they had died? To heaven or to hell?" she wondered.

Picking up her pen, she began to write about the two men. In her poem she wrote about heaven and hell. On December 21, 1767, a Rhode Island newspaper printed the finished poem. Phillis was thirteen years old.

Looking about Boston, Phillis saw many changes taking place. She wrote more poems as British soldiers marched through the city. She wrote while the citizens and the soldiers shouted insults at each other. Everywhere people talked of war.

In August a British preacher named George Whitefield arrived in Boston. Phillis attended the services with the Wheatleys. She sat in the balcony with the other slaves and listened carefully. She liked what she heard and looked forward to other meetings. But one Sunday morning in late September, a man rode up King Street shouting, "Whitefield is dead! Whitefield is dead!"

The thought of death shocked Phillis. "Mr. Whitefield is in heaven, but where will I be when I die?" she thought. "He showed me the way of salvation. I must follow."

Phillis wrote a poem describing her sorrow over Mr. Whitefield's death. Many colonial newspapers printed the poem, and it was even published in London, England.

The important men of Boston were amazed. "This girl has been in our land for only nine years," they said. "She could not write this!"

Many of them came to the Wheatley home to speak to Phillis. Only when they talked to her did they believe that she had actually written the poem.

On August 18, 1771, Phillis was baptized in the Old South Church. "Ten years ago I saw my mother pour out offerings to the sun," she said. "God's mercy has brought me from those heathen practices to His salvation."

Phillis wrote many more poems, often staying up late into the night. She began to get sick again, so the Wheatleys sent her into the country, hoping the fresh air would help. But Phillis only grew worse.

Finally the doctor suggested a sea voyage. "Perhaps salt air will make her feel better," he said.

Mrs. Wheatley nodded. "Nathaniel has to go to London on business. Phillis can go with him to prepare her poems for publication in London. The Countess of Huntingdon has agreed to be her patron."

So Phillis found herself skimming across the ocean in a passenger ship. In London she had the pleasure of being presented to nobility. She also saw her first volume of poetry go to the printer. But one day a letter came from America. Mrs. Wheatley was very ill. Phillis set sail for America in July.

When Phillis arrived in Boston, Mary took her quickly to Mrs. Wheatley's bedside.

"How are you feeling?" Phillis asked quietly.

Mrs. Wheatley struggled to sit up. "I feel a little better each day," she said. "I'm just glad to have you home, Phillis."

But Mrs. Wheatley did not get better. She grew weaker and weaker. Mary and Phillis stayed by her side.

One month after Phillis had arrived home, Mr. Wheatley called her into his study.

"Phillis," Mr. Wheatley said, "are you happy with us, truly happy?"

"Why, of course," Phillis replied. "Why do you ask?"

"Your English friends think that you should be set free," he answered. "Would you like your freedom, Phillis?"

"I believe that God has planted the love of freedom in every person," Phillis said slowly. "God has released my soul from the bondage of sin. If He wishes, He will release my body in His own way and time. Until that day comes, I will obey you as my master because it pleases God."

"God has answered your prayers," said Mr. Wheatley. "I will have the paper prepared. You will have your freedom."

"Thank you, Mr. Wheatley!" Phillis cried, tears running down her cheeks. "God bless you!"

"Phillis, you have become one of the family." Mr. Wheatley shook his head sadly. "Where will you go now?"

Phillis thought for a moment. Freedom meant that she would have her own lodgings. The money from the sale of her books would be her chief source of income, allowing her time to write another volume for publication. She would be on her own!

But upstairs the woman who had accepted her as a child lay ill, perhaps dying. Phillis turned to Mr. Wheatley. "That can wait," she said. "May I stay and care for my mistress?"

"Of course, Phillis." Mr. Wheatley smiled. "Of course you may stay. Mrs. Wheatley would be heartbroken to lose you now. She loves you."

"And I love her," Phillis replied.

"Then let's go tell her our news. She has been waiting to hear the outcome of our meeting." Mr. Wheatley held out his arm. Together he and Phillis walked up the stairs.

Mrs. Wheatley died shortly afterward, but Phillis remained with the family. War loomed closer and closer. On April 18, 1775, Paul Revere spread the word: "The British are coming!" The war had begun. Phillis continued writing poems; however, there was no longer a market for poetry in war-torn America. Her health grew steadily worse. In December of 1784 Phillis Wheatley died at the age of thirty-one. She is still remembered today for her poetry and for her remarkable ability to learn.

A DARK NIGHT

(based on historical research)

Cast

Narrator	Robert Newman
Billy Dawes	Rachel
Caleb	Joshua Bentley
Dr. Warren	Tom Richardson
Paul Revere	Colonel Conant
British soldier	

Act One

Narrator: The moon had not yet risen on the night of April 18, 1775, as Billy Dawes and a friend hurried through Boston. A cold wind tore at their clothing and reddened their cheeks. At the corner of Hanover Street the men stopped. Off in the distance the faint clanking of British weapons mingled with the dull thud of boots.

Billy Dawes: Mark my words, Caleb, those soldiers are up to no good. Why would they be gathering at North Square after dark?

Caleb: Surely Dr. Warren knows. I wonder why he sent for us.

Narrator: The two patriots glanced up and down the street. Then, sneaking in and out of the shadows to avoid the British soldiers, they made their way to the doctor's house. A small flicker of light fell on the men's faces as Dr. Warren opened the door a crack. Then, unbolting it, he let the two men in.

Dr. Warren: Come in, come in!

Billy Dawes: Sir, North Square is filled with British troops!

Dr. Warren: Yes, yes, I know. We must act now! Can one of you ride across the Neck tonight?

Caleb: That narrow strip of land? That's been occupied by British soldiers for a long time.

Dr. Warren: Yes, but that's the only land route out of the city. The British are making plans to march on Concord to seize our weapons. They are also expecting to find Samuel Adams and John Hancock and arrest them. It's up to you to warn them!

Billy Dawes: I can get across the Neck, sir. I've done plenty of odd jobs for the soldiers camped there. To them I'm just a harmless farmer. They won't think twice about letting me through.

Dr. Warren: Good!

Narrator: Dr. Warren turned to Caleb and spoke urgently.

Dr. Warren: Young man, do you know where Paul Revere lives?

Caleb: His house faces North Square, I believe, sir.

Dr. Warren: Yes, yes. Tell him that I need to see him immediately. Now be off, gentlemen, both of you.

Narrator: The two men slipped out the door and disappeared into the night. Darting along dark alleys, Caleb made his way to the Revere house. He knocked quietly on the door. The door opened just wide enough for him to recognize Paul Revere.

Caleb: Dr. Warren wants to see you immediately, Mr. Revere. The soldiers that had gathered in North Square have gone down to the river.

Narrator: Having spoken quickly and quietly, Caleb left. Without even stopping to put on an overcoat, Paul let himself out the back door. Quietly he followed a crooked course to the doctor's house. A silver moon made the direct route too dangerous. Around ten o'clock he knocked on the doctor's door.

Dr. Warren: Come in, Paul. We must hurry. The British troops are rowing across the Charles River. What plans were you able to make on Sunday with the people at Charlestown?

Paul Revere: They are to watch the belfry tower at North Church. Robert Newman will light one lantern if the British are coming by land, two if they come by sea.

Dr. Warren: Good, good. Get the signal out. Then take your boat across the river. The Charlestown patriots will have a horse waiting for you. You must ride like the wind, warning patriots in every house and village to hide their ammunition. Billy Dawes is already on his way to Lexington by way of the Neck to warn Hancock and Adams. We can't count on his getting through. You must also try to warn them.

Narrator: The two men shook hands. Both knew it would be a dangerous ride.

Act Two

Narrator: Paul paused outside the doctor's house. Should he go home to get an overcoat first? Or should he get the signal message to Robert Newman? The message was more important. Turning quickly on his heels, Paul headed toward Sheafe and Salem streets. At the corner, a shadowy figure stepped out of the darkness.

Paul Revere: Robert, is that you?

Robert Newman: I thought you might come tonight, so I waited outside. What is the message for our Charlestown friends?

Paul Revere: The British are going by boat. They expect to be in Lexington before dawn.

Robert Newman: Then we must hurry. You can depend on me. Two if by sea—right?

Paul Revere: Right! And God bless our land.

Narrator: The two men hurried off, Robert Newman to the tall spire of North Church, and Paul Revere to his home. Pulling on his overcoat and his riding boots, Paul looked from one family member to another. It might be the last time he saw them.

Paul Revere: Son, take care of things while I'm gone. Rachel, my sweet wife, pray for me. I must get through with this message.

Rachel: I am proud of you. America will be blessed by your courage. Ride well, Paul.

Narrator: Paul said good-bye to his family and again slipped out into the night.

Rachel: Paul, you forgot your spurs!

Narrator: But Paul was already gone, his mind occupied by the task that lay before him. His pace quickened as he approached the hiding place of his small boat. Two men looked up quickly as they heard his footsteps.

Joshua Bentley: Paul, I've wrapped your oars in old rags to muffle the sounds.

Tom Richardson: Don't know whether it will do much good. The British ship *Somerset* sits in the middle of the river. With this full moon, it will be a miracle if we are not spotted by her crew.

Paul Revere: We'll trust God to take care of us. Did you see the lantern signal?

Joshua Bentley: You mean the two lanterns from North Church?

Tom Richardson: We saw them shine briefly. I hope Charlestown was watching.

Paul Revere: We'll know once we reach the other side. Let's get going.

Narrator: Without a sound, the boat left the safety of the shadows with the three patriots. Out into the deep waters, out under the bright light of the moon the small boat glided. Slowly, painstakingly, silently the men rowed with muffled oars. At last the shadows of the Charlestown bank welcomed them.

Joshua Bentley: May God speed you this night, Paul Revere!

Paul Revere: Take care, men.

Narrator: Paul leaped onto the bank and hurried to the house of Colonel Conant, where a group of men waited for him. He knocked at the door.

Colonel Conant: Paul! Come in, quickly. We saw the lights from the North Church tower. Our men say the roads to Cambridge and Concord are patrolled by British soldiers.

Paul Revere: Have you heard anything?

Colonel Conant: Some of the officers have been asking the villagers for the location of Clark's house.

Paul Revere: That's where Sam Adams and John Hancock are staying! Dr. Warren was right!

Colonel Conant: They intend to arrest the two men.

Paul Revere: I must get through whether the roads are guarded or not.

Colonel Conant: Come, we have a horse for you, the best horse in Charlestown.

Narrator: Paul hurried outside. Two men led a light-footed horse out of the shadows. Paul quickly adjusted the stirrups and checked the girth. Then he swung into the saddle.

Colonel Conant: Be careful! Watch for the patrols!

Narrator: With a wave of his hand, Paul galloped away down the moonlit road. He had not gone far before he saw the glint of moonlight on rifles. Two British soldiers blocked the road.

British soldier: Halt! Who goes there?

Narrator: Paul didn't answer. He dug his heels into his horse's sides and turned sharply into the open fields. One of the soldiers spurred his horse after him.

British soldier: Halt! Halt, I say, in the name of the king!

Narrator: Closer and closer the soldier came. The hard breathing of his horse made chills chase along Paul's spine. Then, ahead of him, Paul saw a pond. Kicking his horse, he headed straight for it. At the last moment he veered sharply to the left. The British soldier galloped on, not able to stop. Down the muddy bank slid horse and rider. Paul grinned to himself, rode his horse around the pond, and headed toward Lexington. At every farmhouse and village along the way he shouted his message.

Paul Revere: The redcoats are coming! Awake! Awake!

Narrator: Windows flew open and nightcapped heads popped out. Men dressed quickly and grabbed their guns. Church bells pealed out the message. Meanwhile, Paul rode hard for Lexington to warn Sam Adams and John Hancock so that the British would not find them.

As for the British, their surprise attack became a disaster. American minutemen, hiding in bushes by the side of the road, took easy aim at the soldiers marching in straight rows. The British army finally retreated and raced back for the safety of Boston. The War for Independence had begun.

Lullaby

The long canoe
Toward the shadowy shore,
One . . . two . . .
Three . . . four . . .
The paddle dips,
Turns in the wake,
Pauses, then
Forward again,
Water drips
From the blade to the lake.
Nothing but that,
No sound of wings;
The owl and bat
Are velvet things.
No wind awakes,
No fishes leap,
No rabbits creep
Among the brakes.

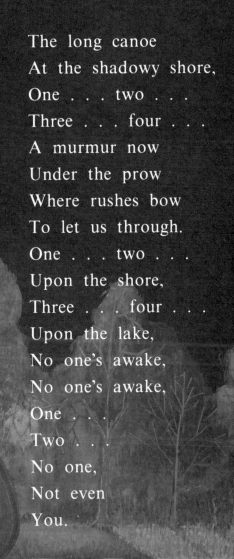

The long canoe
At the shadowy shore,
One . . . two . . .
Three . . . four . . .
A murmur now
Under the prow
Where rushes bow
To let us through.
One . . . two . . .
Upon the shore,
Three . . . four . . .
Upon the lake,
No one's awake,
No one's awake,
One . . .
Two . . .
No one,
Not even
You.

Robert Hillyer

Captured!

At Boonesborough in the summer of 1776, corn grew tall, apple and peach trees stood in neat rows, and chickens pecked busily at the ground around the log cabins. There had been no Indian attacks since December. Sunday afternoon was peaceful and hot. The water of the Kentucky River flowed past the settlement, cool and inviting.

"Indians!"

The canoe rocked gently as Jemima Boone dipped her sore foot into the cool water. "This feels good," she said with a sigh. "Let's paddle a little farther downstream."

"Should we?" asked sixteen-year-old Betsey Callaway. "Our daddies told us not to go too far downstream."

"Oh, I know why you are worried. You don't want to miss Samuel Henderson when he comes courting," Jemima said. She lifted her foot out of the water and inspected the jagged cut on the bottom. "I'll never walk barefoot in cane stubble again."

166

"Betsey wouldn't go barefoot. She wouldn't leave her good shoes at home," teased Fanny Callaway, who was two years younger than her sister. "She wants to look like a city girl for her husband-to-be."

Betsey blushed and kept paddling. "Just wait until you meet someone you like," she told the two younger girls.

"Daddy says I'm too young to have a sweetheart," Jemima said.

"Your sister is my age," Betsey replied. "She's been married for more than a year. You'll change your mind soon enough."

"I don't want to think about that now," Jemima replied. "Let's sing."

At Jemima's suggestion the three girls began singing their favorite hymns. As they sang, Betsey and Fanny's paddles kept time with the music. Slowly the canoe floated on downstream.

The last hymn ended just as Fanny spotted colorful wildflowers on the bank. "Let's pick some flowers," she said.

Jemima looked at the thick cane on the river's edge. Dark, forested hills rose behind the cane. "Let's turn back," she said uneasily. "We've gone too far. Daddy will be angry with us for being so careless."

Betsey and Fanny shoved with all their might. Their struggles freed the canoe, but it drifted toward the canebrake. Suddenly five Indians burst from their hiding place among the canes. One Indian waded into the water and grabbed the buffalo-hide rope at the front of the canoe.

"Let us be!" Jemima screamed. "Put down that rope!"

As the Indian pulled the canoe toward the shore, Fanny tried to beat him off with her paddle, but it broke. All three girls were screaming with fear.

The other Indians quickly ran into the waist-deep water, clapping rough hands over the girls' mouths. They dragged the kicking, struggling girls through the water and up the bank.

When they were safely hidden in the cane, the Indians raised their knives and tomahawks. One of the warriors grabbed Betsey's dark hair.

"Pretty squaw," said the Indian. "No scream."

Betsey's eyes opened wide and her mouth closed tightly. Jemima's and Fanny's mouths also snapped shut.

The Indians rushed the girls through the cane and into the forest. By the time they reached high ground, Jemima had calmed down and was thinking fast. At the top of a hill she dug her bare heels into the hard earth and said loudly, "I won't take one more step. You can kill me if you wish. Walking on this sore foot is worse than death."

"You think we no hear you?" the leader asked in his low voice. "You walk."

Jemima shook her head, crossed her arms, and sat down. "I'm not taking another step on this sore foot."

The Indian warriors waved their tomahawks, but Jemima would not budge. Finally the leader made a sign. Two Indians handed their extra moccasins to Jemima and Fanny.

"Put on moccasins," said the Indian leader.

Jemima and Fanny quickly laced up their borrowed moccasins. As Jemima stood up, three warriors pulled out knives and stepped toward the girls.

"Squaws no run," they said as they cut off the girl's long skirts at their knees.

"Oh, no! That's my best dress," Betsey cried. "You've ruined it!"

"Long journey . . . we walk fast," the Indian said.

"Well, I won't run through the woods and canebrakes like this," Jemima said, looking at her bare legs. "The underbrush and briars will tear up my legs."

The leader made a sign to the warrior who had picked up the torn pieces of the girls' skirts.

"Wrap legs," he said.

As she wrapped the cloth around her legs to protect them, Jemima wondered about the leader. "The other Indians are Shawnees, but he is a Cherokee," she thought. "He speaks much better English than the others. Who is he? Where have I seen him before?"

Suddenly Jemima remembered the Cherokee chief, Hanging Maw, who had often visited the Boone cabin in North Carolina. This chief had brought her pretty shells and feathers. He had eaten bread and stew with her family.

"Do you remember me, Hanging Maw?" Jemima asked the chief. "When I was a little girl, you brought me gifts. I'm Jemima Boone, Daniel Boone's daughter."

"You Boone's girl?" asked Hanging Maw.

"Yes," Jemima replied.

Hanging Maw pointed to Betsey and Fanny. "And they too?"

"Yes," Jemima lied. She hoped that Hanging Maw would treat the Callaway girls better if he thought they were Boones.

Hanging Maw laughed. "How de do!" he said, as he shook each girl's hand. "Well, we do pretty good for this time."

The Shawnees also shook hands with the girls. "How de do! How de do!"

"Come now," said Hanging Maw. "We go."

Traveling North

Any hope of being released disappeared as Hanging Maw took Jemima's arm. Two of the Shawnees grabbed Betsey and Fanny. Each Indian entered the nearby canebrake from a different spot. Jemima knew that meant the Indians were leaving five trails through the canebrake to confuse her father. "Will I see him again?" she wondered. "Will I see any of my family again?"

Jemima gasped for breath as Hanging Maw pulled her along faster. The tall, thick canes shut out most of the light and air. Snakes sometimes crawled near her feet and mosquitoes buzzed around her hot face all the time.

At last Hanging Maw pulled Jemima from the dry canebrake. Just ahead, the other Indians were waiting with Betsey and Fanny.

The Indians did not stop to rest. One warrior walked behind to guard the rear. The other four Indians led their captives down the middle of cool streams and across the dark hills.

Jemima remembered the things that her father had taught her. She noticed that the afternoon sun was in the west. She also studied the moss and vines that grew on the trees.

"Let's see," Jemima thought. "Moss grows on the dark north side of a tree, while thicker vines grow on the sunny south side."

When she knew the direction they were walking, Jemima asked, "May we have something to eat?"

Hanging Maw stopped and gave the girls some of the dried meat from his pouch. "Eat," he said.

"We have been walking north all afternoon. Where are you taking us?" Jemima asked as she bit down on the chewy meat.

"Shawnee towns . . . north," Hanging Maw replied. "Pretty squaws of Wide Mouth Boone will make good wives for Shawnee warriors."

With these words, Hanging Maw returned to the front of the column. He led his small group through more canebrakes, always making more than one trail.

When they were back under the trees, Betsey and Fanny walked beside Jemima. They held her up when she stumbled. Once Betsey whispered in despair, "How will our daddies find us?"

"Daddy is the best tracker in Kentucky," Jemima whispered back. "I am sure that he is trailing us. He knows that the Indians would kill us before they'd let white men take us. He will rescue us when it is safe."

The sun was beginning to go down when
Hanging Maw stopped for the night near a
gurgling mountain stream. Before the chief lay
down, he tied the girls' arms together behind their
backs and set each of them against a different tree.

"One end of thong tied to tree. We hold other
end," said Hanging Maw. "Squaws no run."

"My foot hurts dreadfully, and you have bound
my arms too tightly," Jemima said, almost in tears.

Hanging Maw pulled off
Jemima's moccasin. The chief
unwrapped his headband,
rinsed it in the cool water,
and washed Jemima's foot.
Then he reached into his pouch.

"Good medicine," he said
as he rubbed the mixture on
Jemima's wound.

When he had spread the mixture evenly, Hanging Maw collected moss and bark from a nearby log. Carefully, he placed the cool moss over the wound. Then he wrapped the elm bark and his wet headband around Jemima's foot.

"Now sleep," said Hanging Maw.

"But what about this rope?" Jemima asked. "Won't you loosen it?"

"No," said Hanging Maw with a grunt. He picked up one end of the rope and lay down. The sky was dark now. Jemima couldn't see the other two girls, but she could hear a sob now and then that could not be muffled. Soon she heard Hanging Maw's heavy breathing. Jemima thought of her oldest brother, James, who had been killed by Indians three years before. One of the Indians who had killed James had even been a friend of the Boones, like Hanging Maw. The tears that Jemima had held back all day began to fall.

"Tears won't save us," she thought, blinking her eyes. Softly she began to hum "At Home With God Anywhere." "What will morning bring?" she wondered as owls hooted and wolves howled. "Will it bring Daddy or death?"

Leaving a Trail

When the first rays of the sun appeared over the mountain, the Indians untied the sleepy girls.

"May we wash?" Jemima asked.

Hanging Maw nodded. "Squaws no run," he warned, patting his rifle.

The three girls walked the short distance to the stream. They cupped their hands and lifted the refreshing water to their lips. When they had finished drinking, they splashed themselves with the cool water.

Suddenly Jemima plopped down on the bank. "Help me wash my foot," she said in a loud voice.

The girls carefully unwrapped Hanging Maw's "bandage." Then Betsey dipped her handkerchief into the water and began washing the wound. "It looks much better this morning," she said.

"It feels much better," Jemima said softly. "Keep washing my foot and listen closely. I have a plan."

"What is it?" asked Betsey.

"I'm sure that the men are close behind us," Jemima replied. "We must leave signs for them to follow."

"How?" asked Fanny.

"Fanny, you break twigs," said Jemima. "Betsey, dig your heels into the mud and drop pieces of your handkerchief."

"But what if the Indians see us?" Betsey asked as she finished washing Jemima's foot.

Before Jemima could answer, Hanging Maw said, "Pretty squaws. Come."

Jemima wrapped the headband around her foot, put on her moccasin, and stood up. "Watch yourselves," she whispered.

Once again, the Indians made five trails. But on this morning the girls smiled to themselves. They had a plan!

As they walked along the trail, the girls left signs. Betsey dug her heels into the damp earth. Fanny lagged behind and broke twigs. Jemima fell into thorn bushes, letting sharp thorns snag pieces of her dress.

Suddenly the Indian at the rear pushed past the girls. He carried small pieces of cloth.

Hanging Maw stared at the torn spots in Jemima's dress. "What's this?" he asked.

"My foot hurts," Jemima replied. "Sometimes when I hold on to a bush, a thorn snags my dress."

Hanging Maw said nothing, but he and the other Indians began watching the girls more carefully. When Betsey again stepped in mud, they wiped away her heelprints and broke off her wooden heels. When Fanny broke twigs, they bent the twigs in the opposite direction. When Jemima snagged her dress, they picked the cloth off the thorns.

All morning the girls tried to leave signs. Sometimes, when they were very clever, they left signs that the Indians' sharp eyes missed.

Once Hanging Maw saw Betsey press the sole of her shoe into the damp earth. As he bent over to wipe away the print, she tossed a piece of her tattered skirt under a bush.

Jemima also left many signs. During the morning she often screamed loudly and fell into the bushes, breaking hundreds of twigs. "Oh! My poor foot!" she would say when the Indians waved their tomahawks.

Clumsy Riders

At noon the Indians found a stray pony in the woods. Hanging Maw slipped a rope over the pony's head and then lifted Jemima onto the pony's back.

"Pretty squaw ride," he said, as he led the pony over the narrow trail.

Jemima grabbed the pony's thick mane. She wobbled from side to side as the pony trotted behind Hanging Maw. When the Indians were not watching, she pinched the pony.

"Help! I'm falling!" Jemima shouted as the pony stood up on its hind legs. A second later she slid to the ground.

The Indians laughed heartily at such a "clumsy" girl. They picked her up, brushed her off, and set her back on the pony.

At the next hill Jemima slid off again. This time the Indians smiled weakly. Hanging Maw picked up Jemima and set her on the pony. At his signal, one of the warriors set Fanny in front of her. Another warrior set Betsey behind her.

"Pretty squaws sit on pony," Hanging Maw said.

Jemima smiled. A short time later all three girls screamed and tumbled to the ground.

The Indians frowned and grumbled among themselves. At last one warrior sat on the pony. He grabbed the pony's mane and pressed his knees tightly against the animal's sides.

"Watch," said Hanging Maw to the girls.

Jemima laughed as the warrior rode around and around with his toes almost touching the ground.

"I can do that," she said.

Jemima grabbed the pony's mane. She pressed her knees against the pony's sides.

"Good," said Hanging Maw.

Jemima bit her lip as the pony trotted. For ten minutes she wobbled from side to side. Then she pinched the pony again. Jemima flew backwards through the air and landed on an Indian.

The pony finally grew impatient with the strange people around him. The next time Jemima pinched him and slid down his back, he snorted and bit Hanging Maw.

"Go," said Hanging Maw. He slapped the angry pony and sent it galloping through the woods.

Jemima carefully picked herself up from the bush where she had fallen. "Surely Daddy will find us now," she thought as she rubbed the bruises that covered her body.

At nine o'clock on Tuesday morning the Indians and their captives crossed a small stream. An hour later one of the Indians shot a buffalo and cut out the hump.

"We cook at next water," said Hanging Maw.

"That means they'll make a fire," Jemima thought. Her heart sank. "Why are the Indians so careless today?"

"Have you heard the Indians talking about Boonesborough?" Fanny whispered. "They are saying that many Indians are supposed to have attacked the fort."

"Something must have happened," Jemima replied. "Daddy should have rescued us by now."

The girls walked the next few miles in silence. As the sun rose higher and higher in the sky, their spirits sank lower and lower. "The men are not coming for us," they thought.

At noon the girls and the hungry Indians waded down a mountain stream until they came to a small creek. "Sit," said Hanging Maw to the girls.

Betsey leaned against a giant oak tree. She sighed and slowly lowered herself to the hard earth.

Fanny and Jemima crumpled to the ground. They lay their heads in Betsey's lap. Tears trickled down their dirty cheeks onto the torn folds of Betsey's best dress.

Rescue

When the girls were settled, the Indians began fixing their noon meal. Hanging Maw walked to the stream to fill a kettle with water. One Indian stood guard on a small mound in the rear. The other Indians gathered wood, kindled a fire, and put a stick through the buffalo hump.

At first the guard stood on his mound and searched the bushes for enemies. Then, when the meat began sizzling, he put down his rifle and strolled toward the fire.

Jemima watched the guard squat down beside the fire and begin sewing the rips in his moccasins. "I wish that I had obeyed Daddy," she said to the other girls. "I'm sorry we ever paddled down that river. I don't want to live like an Indian for the rest of my life."

Suddenly a shot rang out. Jemima sat up just in time to see the guard drop his moccasins and tumble to the ground.

More shots were fired. The wounded guard crawled into a nearby canebrake.

"That's Daddy!" cried Jemima as the rifles cracked.

The Indians around the fire dashed for the canebrake. The men in the bushes yelled, "Run, gals, run!"

Jemima jumped up, screaming with joy. She ran toward the men in the bushes. Betsey and Fanny followed at her heels.

The girls had run only a few feet when Daniel Boone shouted, "Fall down!"

Instantly, the three girls fell flat on their stomachs. Just as they hit the ground, a tomahawk sailed over Betsey's head. Knives fell on all sides.

When the Indians retreated, the men rushed into the camp, and Jemima ran into her father's

arms. Samuel Henderson scooped Betsey up into a hug.

While the men made sure that the girls had not been harmed, the crashing and rustling in the canebrake stopped.

"The Indians are escaping," some men said. "It shouldn't be hard to capture them. At least two Indians were wounded."

"They have left behind everything except one rifle," said Daniel Boone as he hugged Jemima. "Let them go. We've got our girls back."

Fanny asked, "Where's Daddy?"

"We knew the Indians would take you north," Daniel explained. "He and some horsemen rode straight to the Licking River. They are waiting to ambush the Indians. When they see that we have rescued you, they will join us."

While Daniel Boone talked, Betsey stared at Samuel. Finally she asked, "What's wrong with your beard, Samuel?"

"I had shaved only half of my beard when I heard your screams on Sunday," Samuel said with a laugh. "I haven't shaved since then."

"I was asleep when you girls screamed," Daniel Boone added. "I followed you in my bare feet and Sunday clothes. I didn't have my moccasins until the women sent our hunting clothes."

"Is Mama safe?" Jemima asked. "We thought the Indians had attacked Boonesborough. Hanging Maw boasted that many Indians were on their way to the fort."

"Everyone was safe when we left," said her father. "I hope the Indians have not attacked since then."

"What took you so long?" Fanny asked.

Daniel pushed his felt hat to the back of his head. "We have had a hard time tracking you," he explained. "The Indians left behind many trails and false signs. We finally decided to head straight north."

"Did you see our signs?" asked Jemima.

"Yes, we often came upon a broken twig, a scrap of cloth, or a heelprint. When we saw your signs, we knew that we were on the right trail," Daniel said. "I was sure that my Mima would know how to mark a trail."

Jemima smiled at her father's praise.

Now that the girls were safe, many of the men wanted to hurry back to Boonesborough to make sure that their families had not been attacked.

"We must finish building the fort," they said.

Daniel looked at the tired girls and rubbed his chin. "The girls have not slept much in two nights," he said. "We will walk a short distance and then make camp. The men we left behind should be able to hold the fort until we return."

"Thank you, Daddy," Jemima said. "I'm sorry that I disobeyed you. You told me not to go far downstream."

"I'm so glad that you're safe that all is forgiven," said Daniel.

"I will never forget these last three days," Jemima replied. "They will always remind me to obey."

Daniel Boone

Daniel Boone at twenty-one
Came with his tomahawk, knife, and gun
Home from the French and Indian War
To North Carolina and the Yadkin shore.
He married his maid with a golden band,
Builded his house and cleared his land;
But the deep woods claimed their son again
And he turned his face from the homes of men.
Over the Blue Ridge, dark and lone,
The Mountains of Iron, the Hills of Stone,
Braving the Shawnee's jealous wrath,
He made his way on the Warrior's Path.
Alone he trod the shadowed trails;
But he was lord of a thousand vales
As he roved Kentucky, far and near,
Hunting the buffalo, elk, and deer.
What joy to see, what joy to win
So fair a land for his kith and kin,
Of streams unstained and woods unhewn;
"Elbow room!" laughed Daniel Boone.

Arthur Guiterman

THE HUNT

The Indian boy
moved carefully,
walking lightly
through the forest.
Not a leaf
shivered at his passing,
not a twig
snapped.

Keeping
to the shelter
of the overhanging trees,
the boy skirted
a moonlit meadow.
He came
to a small hill
and stopped
to look out
over the meadow.
Watching.
Waiting.
But no shadows moved
on the grass-covered slopes.

The boy knelt
beside a tree
to wait.
A chipmunk
ran
along the branch
above the boy,
chattering.
The boy's eyes
never left the meadow.
He watched.
Waited.
Quiet.

Slowly
the sky
above the meadow
turned gray
then silver
then pink.

A movement
along one
of the slopes
caught his eye.
A deer came
over a rise of ground
and
trotted
through the grass.

The deer,
upwind
and
sensing no danger,
began to graze.
The boy
waited,
watching
the graceful movements
of the deer.
It was a young stag,
muscles rippling
under soft skin.
From time to time
it stopped grazing
to arch
its neck
and
prance
about,
proudly
tossing its antlers.

It stopped,
head held high,
to sniff the morning air.
The boy
stiffened,
but the light breeze
ruffled his hair
around his face,
and
he relaxed.

The boy
grinned
as the deer jumped
into the air
and
landed lightly,
running along
the rise of ground.
His blood
surged,
his body
eager
to race with the deer.
"Wait,"
said his mind,
"wait."

At full light
the signal
for the hunt
would be given.
Through the forest
he and his brothers
would drive the deer,
through the mountain gap
where the hunters
waited,

arrows sharpened
and bows
newly strung.
The boy
shivered
with excitement
for
this
was his first hunt.

As the sky
reddened
he left the tree
and moved
into a better position
to drive the deer.
He was ready
when a distant
shout
broke the silence.
The stag's head
flew up
and he froze,
quivering.
The boy
stepped
out of the shelter
of the trees.

He
yelled
and ran
toward the stag.
The stag
spun,
hooves tearing the grass
as he raced
across the meadow
to the forest
on the other side.
The boy
followed,
running
in great bounds,
shouting
with a joy
that was too great
to
contain.
Dew
from the grass
sprayed his face.
Air
whipped into his lungs.
Light
glowed around him as he ran.

Ahead of him
the deer
leaped a
fallen log
and disappeared
between the trees.

The boy
slowed
to a steady lope.
His chest heaved;
his eyes searched
the trees
and the bushes.
A crash
in the underbrush
turned him
to the right,
and he leaped
over fallen logs
and branches
to head the deer
back
into the trees.

Squirrels scolded
angrily,
and birds screamed
as they raced
through the forest.
But
neither deer
nor boy
heard.
At last the deer
was too far away
for the boy
to see.
The boy
walked
to slow
his labored
breathing.

The Hunt   197

When his breath
was even
and
he could again
hear
the sounds
of the forest,
he stopped
to listen
for the deer.
He heard
only
the small animals,
disturbed
by the noise
of his passing.

He walked on,
following
a trail
of snapped twigs
and hoofprints
in soft dirt.
Once
he lost
the trail
at a rushing
stream.

With surprise
he discovered
the stag's hoofprints
downstream.
He climbed
the bank,
senses sharpened,
more aware
of his prey.

Once
a rustle
in the bushes
made his heart
pound,
but it was
only a beaver
waddling back
to the stream.

198

Often
he heard shouts
not far behind
him
and knew
his brothers
were driving
deer
toward the gap
where the hunters
waited.

When he came
upon the stag,
it was almost
by accident.
The deer
had doubled back
on its trail
and
had stopped
to listen
to the boy's progress
through the underbrush.
It
stood
motionless
on the boy's left,

almost
hidden
by tangled vines.

The boy
stopped
and
waited,
sweat running
down his back.
He saw
the pulse
beat
in the stag's
neck,
hard
and
fast.
The stag stared
at the boy,
eyes
wide with fear,
and trembled
as crashing
and
shouts
echoed
through the forest
behind them.

Wondering,
the boy
held out a hand
as if
to touch
the frightened deer.
The stag
hung
for a moment,
caught between
a sense
of danger upwind
and certain danger
before him.

Then
the boy
made a small sound,
and
the stag
whirled and raced
toward the mountain gap
where the hunters
waited,
ready.

The crashing
sounds
behind the boy
grew louder,
louder.
Three deer
charged past
on his right,
followed
by the boy's brothers.

Once
again
the boy
began to run,
great bounding leaps
over logs and branches.
Plunging past trees,
scattering dry leaves,
he heard his voice
above his brothers',
the high,
piercing cry
of the
hunt.

THE GREAT
ELECTRIC EEL

Ferdie and Wally Meet the Cowboy

Grandpa and Grandma Grouper were coming to supper tonight, so Mother Fish was busy getting everything ready. Ferdie was with Father in front of the house. He was getting all the stones out of the yard so that Father could mow the seaweed.

Ferdie was almost finished with his job when he heard Mother cry, "Oh, dear!" She called out to Ferdie, "Ferdie, I ran out of sauce for the shrimp gumbo, and you know how much Grandpa likes shrimp gumbo. Will you please go down to the corner store and pick up another jar of sauce for me?"

Father said, "Go ahead, son. I can finish the job myself." He handed Ferdie some money.

"May I ask Wally if he wants to go with me?" Ferdie asked.

"Yes," said Father. "But don't be gone long!"

Ferdie swam over to the coral house next door and got Wally. The two friends went off to the store. They liked going to the store because the owner, Mr. Lobster, always gave them a box of fish flakes to share.

Wally and Ferdie got the sauce and swam to the counter. Mr. Lobster pretended (as he often did) to forget to give them their fish flakes, but with a twinkle in his eye he handed them the box at last. Ferdie and Wally thanked him and turned toward the door.

"Oops, excuse me, mister," Ferdie said. He had bumped right into a big fish with whiskers on his chin and a big cowboy hat.

"That's all right, son, but you do pack quite a wallop," said the stranger. He regained his balance and said, "You're almost powerful enough to bring down a wild sea horse!"

"Have you seen wild sea horses, mister?" asked Ferdie with wide eyes.

"Oh, sure, son. I've not only seen 'em; I've ridden 'em," said the cowboy.

"Wow!" exclaimed Wally.

"And if you think sea horses are somethin', young fellers, you'd really have bulging eyeballs if you'd seen the Great Electric Eel like I have!"

As if wild sea horses weren't enough, the mention of the Great Electric Eel really fired their imaginations. "You've really seen him?" asked Ferdie.

"Sure have, sonny," boasted the cowboy. "Lit up the place with more 'lectricity than it would take to dry yer fins at the bottom of the ocean."

"Wowee!" said Wally.

Ferdie would have loved to have heard more, but he remembered that they had to hurry home, so the two little fish said good-bye and swam away.

It was a wonderful supper. Grandpa really enjoyed the shrimp gumbo. "Mighty fine gumbo, Pearl," Grandpa told Ferdie's mom. "That sauce was just perfect."

After the meal the family went into the living room to visit. Ferdie sat next to Grandpa. "Hey, Grandpa," Ferdie asked, "Have you ever heard of the Great Electric Eel?"

"I surely have, Ferdie. He lives in the Coral Cave. My old friend, Mr. Sea Turtle, told me how that ol' eel attacked him once—tried to give him a shock," Grandpa chuckled.

"Did it hurt him?" asked Ferdie.

"Oh, no," said Grandpa. "Turtles are safe from him as long as they're inside their thick shells. And old Mr. Sea Turtle probably has the thickest shell in these parts."

"Oh," sighed Ferdie. Then he added with a flip of his tail, "I want to go see the Great Eel myself, Grandpa!"

"Oh, no you don't," Grandpa answered gruffly. "He's much too dangerous for any fish to tangle with, much less a small fry like you."

"But it would be so exciting! Grandpa, I want to go see him light up the whole Coral Cave, just like I've heard he can do."

"Now just you listen, young fish," Grandpa replied. "You had better get that idea out of your head right this minute, before I see to it that your father fries your scales right here in this living room!"

"Yes, sir," Ferdie sighed quietly.

Before long, Grandpa and Grandma had to go home, and Ferdie had to go to bed. "Tomorrow is a school day," his mother reminded him.

That night until he went to sleep Ferdie could think of nothing else but the glowing electric eel in his colorful coral cave.

The Boys Take a Ray-Taxi

After breakfast the next morning, Ferdie was ready to start another day at school. Father Fish kissed Mother Fish good-bye and opened the door to go off to work. Wally was coming up the doorstep. "Hello, Mr. Fish. Is Ferdie ready to go?"

"Yes, here he comes," said Father.

"Oops, I almost forgot," said Ferdie. He went back to get his lunch money and kiss his mother good-bye. "Bye, Dad."

"Have a nice day, son," Mr. Fish waved as Wally and Ferdie swam off to school.

Every day on their way to school, the two little fish passed old Mr. Sea Turtle's house. This particular morning Ferdie and Wally had already been talking about the Great Electric Eel. So when he saw Mr. Sea Turtle's house, Ferdie felt even more disappointed that he was just going to school instead of to the Coral Cave.

Suddenly Wally exclaimed, "Hey, let's go see Mr. Sea Turtle and ask him to take us to see the Great Eel today."

"But we're supposed to go to school, Wally."

"This could be like a field trip," Wally said.

Ferdie stopped. "Well . . . ," he said, thinking how great it would be to tell all his friends that they had seen the Electric Eel . . . . "Okay, let's see if he'll take us."

They floated up the old wooden steps and knocked on the door.

"Just a minute," came the voice from inside. Then the door opened, and Mr. Sea Turtle peered out. "How can I help you young fish?" asked the thick-shelled old turtle.

"Well, uh," Ferdie sputtered, "we kind of, uh, well, um . . ."

"Yes?" said the turtle politely. His baggy eyes seemed to look right through Ferdie.

Finally the little fish blurted out, "We want you to take us to the Coral Cave to see the Great Electric Eel light up the ocean with more electricity than it would take to dry your fins in ocean water, if you could, 'cause it would be so exciting, and we'd really like it, so can you take us please, Mr. Sea Turtle . . . if you don't mind?"

"Just a minute, now, young fishes," said Mr. Sea Turtle. "Isn't today a school day for youngsters like you?"

Neither Ferdie nor Wally dared to look up into those wise eyes. Finally Wally volunteered, "It's kind of a, um . . . holiday today."

"Oh, really!" The old turtle raised an eyebrow.
Both Wally and Ferdie looked down at their fins.
"Well, holiday or not, two youngsters like you
have no business spying on a dangerous eel who'd
just love to turn you into a fish fry. Now you
two run along and stay out of trouble!"

Mr. Sea Turtle closed the door and left them
on the porch. "Wally, you never should have lied
to him," Ferdie said as they swam slowly away. "I
think you made him angry."

"Yeah, I guess. And now we'll never get to see
the Great Eel," Wally grumbled. "Unless . . ." His
face lighted up. "How much lunch money do you
have, Ferdie?"

"The same as always," Ferdie replied. "But what are you thinking?"

"We could pay a ray-taxi to take us there. They know where everything is!" Wally exclaimed.

"I don't know, Wally. Maybe we just ought to forget the whole thing."

"You aren't getting scared, are you?"

When Wally asked that, Ferdie's fins bristled. "Of course not!" he said. Then he added a little less boldly, "Let's go!"

Ray-taxies always seemed a little suspicious-looking to Ferdie, but at least they didn't ask many questions. Ferdie and Wally found one just a couple of blocks away. "H-hello, Mister Ray," Ferdie said.

"The name's Sting Ray, kid," replied the ray in a gravelly voice. "Whaddya want?"

"We'd like you to take us to the Coral Cave and back, Mr. Sting Ray."

"The Coral Cave? Is that where the Great Electric Eel lives?" asked the ray.

"Uh, I think he moved," Wally blurted out. Ferdie frowned at Wally.

"Round trip'll be twenty-four cockle shells if ya stay less than an hour," grunted the ray. That was all the money they had, and that was with Ferdie's allowance thrown in, but the two little fish agreed and hopped on the ray-taxi's back.

"Hold on tight," grumbled Mr. Ray. "Ya fall off, and ya still have to pay full price. Company policy." With that remark they were off with a jerk.

Ferdie thought that his fins couldn't hold on any longer when at last they arrived at the Coral Cave.

Danger at Coral Cave

"This place is creepy," said the ray uneasily. "You sure that eel doesn't live here any more?"

"We'll meet you back here in less than an hour," Ferdie said quickly. He and Wally started swimming slowly toward the cave. Indeed it was spooky. They didn't see any other fish at all swimming around in the water. Everything was dark and murky.

"The cave almost looks like it has teeth!" whispered Wally as they swam silently through several dingy corridors. They could imagine how bright and beautiful the coral would look if only there were some light.

Suddenly Wally stopped. "I th-think I hear something down that skinny little corridor," he whispered.

"You g-go ahead, Wally," Ferdie stammered.

They swam along the narrow coral walls until they came to the opening of a huge cavern that had a twisted forest of coral growing in it from the ceiling and the floor. In the dim light, a long black shape sniffed among the piles of rock and bone.

"It's got to be the Great Eel," whispered Wally. "But he's not glowing."

"He doesn't glow all the time. Just wait," Ferdie whispered back.

In their anticipation the two little fish almost forgot how afraid they were. The eel seemed to be muttering to himself and getting very frustrated, as if he couldn't find something. He grunted suddenly and—flash!—he started to glow. The Coral Cave burst into reds, oranges, blues, and purples, brighter than any lights the two young fish had ever seen! The eel was brighter than lightning, and he hummed while he glowed!

"Wow!" exclaimed Wally rather loudly. Then their hearts almost stopped as the eel looked up from the floor—right at them.

"Scram!" cried Ferdie. The two fish scrambled through the corridors, the eel flashing wildly somewhere behind them. Then everything went dark again.

"Maybe we lost him!" panted Wally.

"Maybe *we're* lost!" cried Ferdie.

In their excitement they had forgotten how to get out! They swam fearfully along the coral hallway, looking for the right way.

Suddenly in the darkness there was a bright flash. It was the eel—he was right behind them! His fiery eyes narrowed as he snarled at them.

"There's the way out!" cried Ferdie as the eel's light filled the hallway. They swam faster than their fins had ever taken them before, but still the Great Eel was behind them, snaking closer and closer!

"If we can just get to Mr. Ray!" panted Ferdie. They swam through the cave's jagged entrance and headed toward the place where they had left the ray.

"Where is he?" yelled Wally. There was the ray, nearly out of sight, quickly swimming away to save his life. Their hearts sank in despair as the eel crackled and flashed with electricity just a few yards behind them. "Why did we have to come?" sobbed Wally.

Just then a big, funny-shaped container dived right in front of their noses. A wrinkled, baggy-eyed head popped out of one of its holes. "Quick, squeeze into my shell with me!"

It was Mr. Sea Turtle! Wally and Ferdie wiggled in with Mr. Sea Turtle's head, just before the Great Eel rammed into the turtle's thick shell. Sparks flew everywhere, like the Fourth of July!

"You scaly old tank!" growled the badly bruised eel. "You stole my lunch!" And the dark eel limped back toward the cave, snarling as he went.

When Mr. Sea Turtle had swum far away, the two fish popped out of the shell. "Quite a way to celebrate a holiday, eh, young fish?" remarked Mr. Sea Turtle.

Wally hung his head and looked down at his fins. "I'm sorry, Mr. Sea Turtle. I lied to you. Today's not a holiday. We were supposed to be in school."

"Yes, I know that very well, young fish," Mr. Sea Turtle replied, "and I also know that any youngster who thinks he can fool me that easily might also be foolish enough to try to go see the Great Electric Eel on his own." The old turtle's eyes looked right into Ferdie's and Wally's eyes, but somehow they weren't as mean-looking as before.

"Thank you for everything, Mr. Sea Turtle," said Ferdie. "I learned a lot today."

"Yes . . .thank you," said Wally.

"It's time for you two young fish to get back to school," the old turtle reminded them. Together the three friends swam back to town.

Sooner or Later

A gust of cold wind whipped the edge of the tablecloth and swept flames up the stone chimney.

"Close the door quickly, Matthew!" Mother cried, snatching a pot from the flames.

Matthew kicked the door closed behind him and clumped to the woodbox. He dropped the firewood into the box and walked back to hang his coat and hat on the peg by the door. A low whine and scratching on the door made him stop and look at his father.

"Let them in, Matthew," said Father.

When Matthew opened the door, two coonhounds charged into the room. The older dog trotted over to Father and sat down. The younger dog dashed to the fireplace where Samantha sat on the floor. She hugged him around his neck and climbed up on his back. She pulled on his long floppy ears. "Giddap, Sooner!" she yelled. The young coonhound wiggled and turned to lick her face.

Matthew gave a worried look at the older coonhound at his father's knee. "Old Blue's been acting funny all day, Pa. Kinda restless. Maybe he smells Indians."

"Indians!" Rebecca dropped her knitting.

"Injins!" Samantha slid off Sooner's back.

"Matthew, don't scare your sisters like that," said Mother.

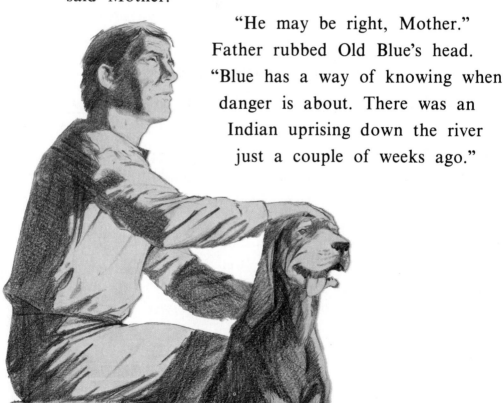

"He may be right, Mother." Father rubbed Old Blue's head. "Blue has a way of knowing when danger is about. There was an Indian uprising down the river just a couple of weeks ago."

"The winter probably makes life just as hard for the Indians as it does for us," Mother added.

"It's been a hard winter," Father agreed. "Even the animals can't find enough to eat."

Old Blue got up and padded quietly to the window, whimpering. Father followed him, opening the wooden shutter and peering out into the twilight.

"Don't see a thing," he said. "Matthew, let's take Blue and look around."

"May we take Sooner, too?" Matthew's tone was questioning, for he knew what his father would say. "After all, he's younger than Old Blue . . ." Matthew's voice trailed off into silence.

"Younger!" Sooner put his head on his paws as Father looked at him in disgust. "He's younger than Blue all right! Almost two years old, and that dog is still nothing but an overgrown puppy. You could never tell he's Blue's son. I don't know why I don't just get rid of him."

"Oh, no, Father! Please let us keep Sooner!" Two heads turned toward Father, and two pairs of begging brown eyes pleaded: Samantha's—and Sooner's.

Mother just smiled. She had heard all this before.

"Well, we'll see," Father said without a smile. "While Blue is warning us of danger, all Sooner does is sit by the fireplace with that foolish grin on his face. Sooner or later that dog has to grow up!"

Matthew smiled, remembering how Sooner got his name. Father had picked him from a litter of pups, saying, "Sooner or later, we'll have another Blue." Samantha, only three at the time, had touched the little puppy and said, "Sooner." Father had laughed and said that "Sooner" would be the puppy's name. Now Sooner was no longer a puppy, but he still hadn't lived up to his name.

Matthew looked at Sooner and sighed. "If we count on you to be another Blue," he thought, "looks like it will be later, not sooner."

Father took his gun from the shelf. Matthew pulled on his coat and whistled to Old Blue. Both dogs came.

"No, Sooner. Stay here with me!" Samantha pulled at Sooner's tail. He turned, and she hugged him around the neck again.

"Mother, the Lord will protect us," Father said, putting his arm around her. "Pray for us while we are gone."

"We will," answered Mother.

Father kissed her gently on the cheek. Then, with Old Blue pulling hard on the leash, he started out. Matthew followed, closing the door behind them.

Rebecca turned to Mother. "Are there really Indians, do you think, Mother?"

"Only the Lord knows, dear," Mother replied. "But we don't need to be afraid. He will protect us." Mother sat down at the table. She pulled Samantha into her lap and put her arm around Rebecca. "Let's pray, girls."

When they were finished, Mother kissed Samantha and put her down. "Now let's get to work," she said. "And while we're working, we can quote some promises from the Bible."

For a while they worked quietly, taking turns quoting verses. From time to time the girls looked toward the door. It seemed like a long time since Father and Matthew had left.

Finally Mother opened the wooden shutter a crack. The girls crowded behind her. Outside all was dark and quiet except for the gusts of wind that swept snowflakes past the window.

"It's snowing," Mother said. "There'll be no tracks to follow. Your father and Matthew will be back soon."

As Mother closed the shutter, they heard a horrible howl from the woods. She gave a startled cry, slammed the shutter, and barred it.

"Indians!" Rebecca said, flinging herself into Mother's arms. Samantha began to cry. Sooner slunk back against the hearth and whimpered.

"Remember that the Lord will protect us, children," Mother's voice trembled. "Rebecca, say another verse."

"I-I can't think of one, Mother." Rebecca hid her face on Mother's shoulder. "Oh . . . well . . . what about Psalm 46:1? 'God is our refuge and strength, a very present help in trouble.'"

"That's a good one," said Mother. "Psalm 91:11: 'He shall give his angels charge over thee, to keep thee in all thy ways.'"

"Samantha?" Mother turned to the sniffling child. "Can you think of a good promise?"

Samantha started to say John 3:16 when the same howl, half-shriek, half-roar sounded from outside again.

"Mother, it's closer!" Rebecca wailed. Samantha burst into tears again, and Sooner howled.

"Children, let's trust the Lord," Mother said firmly. "Now, Rebecca, help me get the stew ready. And Samantha, you can set the table. We want the men to have something hot to eat as soon as they get home."

Rebecca turned obediently toward the fire with Mother. Sooner trotted over to the table and lay on the floor close to Samantha. His eyes turned toward the door, and he panted, as if he were nervous.

There was a scratching sound at the door. A low growl came from Sooner's throat. Mother and Rebecca heard neither as they bent over the fire.

But Samantha heard. She put down the dishes and whispered to Sooner. "That's Old Blue. Daddy must be back."

Samantha hurried across the room. She pushed the latch, and the door creaked open. Mother felt the blast of cold wind and turned around.

With a wild cry a bobcat sprang through the open door. He snarled, turning toward the smell of soup, then—toward Samantha.

The wooden spoon fell from Rebecca's fingers. Mother stood, hand to her throat.

The next moment a black and tan streak came flying across the room. Sooner threw himself upon the bobcat. The wild animal fell back, and the two tumbled to the floor. The bobcat twisted, sinking huge fangs into Sooner's shoulder.

Sooner didn't cry out, but grabbed the bobcat by the neck. The beast turned again and slashed Sooner with fierce claws. Blood trickled from Sooner's side.

Mother and Rebecca ran to Samantha. Over and over the two animals rolled in front of the door, blocking the way. Finally the bobcat jerked and became limp. Sooner rolled over and staggered to his feet. He took a few steps and fell at Samantha's feet. He winced as Samantha hugged him.

Quickly Mother shut the door and knelt beside Samantha. "Samantha, dear," she said gently. "Sooner is badly hurt. He needs to rest."

Samantha released the dog and sat down beside him. As Mother and Rebecca bent over Sooner, they heard Blue barking. There was a thud at the door, then another.

Mother opened the wooden shutter a crack and peered outside. Blue was jumping up on the door, barking loudly.

"It's us," Matthew called. "What's going on?"

Mother opened the door, and Blue charged in, bristles standing in ridges along his back. Snarling, he stood over the dead bobcat. Father and Matthew stared first at the bobcat and then at the bleeding dog on the floor.

The next moment was sheer confusion. Old Blue barked and barked. Matthew and Father asked questions. Mother and Samantha and Rebecca all talked at once. Finally Father threw up his hands. "Here, let's get this bobcat outside so Blue will settle down."

Matthew and Father dragged the body of the bobcat outside. Then they came back in and shut the door. Mother explained what had happened. Father let out a low whistle. "So that's what was bothering Old Blue. I guess Sooner is a better dog than I thought. Killed a bobcat! The Lord kept him here to protect you."

Old Blue trotted over to lie down beside Sooner. Father leaned over the young coonhound, looking at his wounds. "He looks pretty bad."

"Sooner's going to be all right," said Samantha. "You'll fix him, won't you, Daddy?"

Mother looked at Father. He shook his head. "I can try. . . ."

Sooner lifted his head and thumped his tail against the floor. Father knelt beside him and gently rubbed his head. "Guess you fooled me, didn't you?" he said quietly, looking at the wounds again. "Looks like you did grow up sooner than I expected. Well, let's see what we can do for Old Blue's son."

Father stood up. "Mother, get some of that salve I used on Blue's wounds last summer. Rebecca, go get some clean cloth. Samantha . . . well, you just hold Sooner's head there. We're going to help Sooner get well."

The Marvelous Mini Horses

Three hundred years ago the kings and queens of Europe raised very small horses. Some of the horses were smaller than a big dog. These "mini" pets grazed in the palace gardens and played with the royal children. Once a team of miniature horses even pulled an empress's carriage through the streets of Paris, France.

When the nobility lost their power, many of them were not able to keep their tiny horses. The pampered animals were sold to people who did not want to keep them as pets. The new owners expected the horses to help them make money. Some of the small horses traveled with circuses; others pulled carts filled with precious ore in the mines of South America.

Since no one was really interested in raising more mini horses, the breed almost disappeared from the earth. Then in the 1900s, Julio César Falabella, a rancher in Argentina, decided to keep the breed alive. He carefully chose the smallest normal-sized horses he could find, hoping that the foals of these normal horses would be smaller than their parents.

Falabella's plan worked. Each new generation of horses became smaller and smaller. After fifteen years of hard work, he finally had his own breed of mini horses.

In 1962 Falabella sent one of his mini horses to President John Kennedy's young daughter, Caroline. Many Americans saw pictures of this tiny horse and wanted to know more about such an unusual animal.

Many years have passed since President Kennedy's time. The mini horse has continued to become more popular each year. More and more mini-horse ranches are being built throughout the United States. People from all over the world are keeping mini horses as pets.

Of course, mini horses are real horses. They look like horses, whinny, snort, and neigh like horses. They even have the barnyard smell of horses. The big difference between normal-sized horses and mini horses is their size. A small horse must measure less than thirty-four inches from the ground to its shoulder to be a true mini horse.

Mini horses reach their full height and strength during their first four years. These little horses are very strong for their size. A normal-sized horse pulls five times its own weight, or thousands of pounds. An adult mini horse can pull just over one thousand pounds, or ten times its "mini" weight.

A mini horse eats the same types of food that a normal horse does, but in smaller amounts.

One quart of oats each day stuffs the hungriest mini horse. A bale of hay lasts more than two months. Even the grass in his owner's backyard will fill a mini horse's tiny stomach.

Mini horses can easily be transported from place to place. Some owners carry their minis in vans. Others let them ride in the cabs of their pickup trucks, staring at the people in passing cars.

Mini horses make good pets. They need little care, can live in any climate, and have a twenty- to thirty-year lifespan. Children love to play with mini horses. Trained minis have learned to "shake hands," stand on their hind legs, and "play dead."

The interest in mini horses has led to an interest in other mini animals. Now many people are raising mini cows, donkeys, goats, and monkeys. Can you think of another animal that would make a good mini-pet?

DEN OF LIONS

Daniel, a godly young Jew, was among the captives brought to Babylon. He served the Lord faithfully over sixty years and became a chief ruler in Babylon. When Darius the Mede conquered Babylon, Daniel continued to have great influence in the government.

When the king made Daniel one of the chief rulers of the land, the other presidents and princes became jealous. "Why should this captive be a ruler over us?" they murmured. "His position rightfully belongs to one of us. He always interferes with our plans. Let's find some way to get rid of him."

Every day they watched Daniel. Every day they looked and looked to see if they could find something he had done wrong. But Daniel was always wise and good and trustworthy.

So evil men gathered for a meeting. "The only way we can find anything against him," one man said, "is in his worship of his God." And then they made a wicked plan.

Before long all these presidents and princes came before King Darius. They bowed and said, "O King Darius, live forever. All the chief men of the kingdom have talked together. We think it would be wise for you to make a decree to test the loyalty of all your subjects. O King, make a decree that for thirty days no one can ask any request of any god or any man except you. If he does, he shall be cast into the den of lions. Make a law, and sign it so that it cannot be changed."

The princes knew that if there was one thing they could catch Daniel doing, it was praying to his God. But they had lied when they said that all of the chief men had talked together. Daniel, second only to the king, had not been part of the decision at all.

King Darius liked the idea of having so much power. He didn't even stop to think about Daniel, so he quickly signed the decree.

Everyone in the kingdom heard about it. Everyone knew that for a whole month they could pray to no one but the king. Daniel heard about it too. But when he found out, he still went up to his room, just as he had always done. He opened his windows and bowed down toward Jerusalem to pray, just as he always had. "O God," he prayed, "I know that the king's decree is wrong. I know that it is still right for me to pray to You. I trust You to care for me as You always have. I thank You for your protection."

But as Daniel prayed, men were watching him. The wicked princes who had made up the decree saw that he broke the law. They rubbed their hands together and said, "We have him now! He wouldn't stop praying even if his life were in danger. And it is!"

Quickly they ran to King Darius. "O King," they said, "is it not true that you signed a decree that no one could pray to anyone but you for a month?"

"That is true," King Darius replied. "And it is a law that cannot be changed."

"But," the men said triumphantly, "Daniel still prays to his God three times a day. He has not regarded the decree that you made."

The king was stunned. "Of course," he thought to himself. "Why didn't I remember that Daniel would pray to his God anyway? I never meant for him to be hurt."

The king sent the princes away. All that day he talked with his counselors and wise men, trying to find some way to rescue Daniel. But there was no way. He had signed the law himself.

At sundown the princes returned. "Your law, O King, cannot be changed," they reminded him.

King Darius knew that all too well. "Bring Daniel here," he said.

Soon gray-haired Daniel stood before the throne, knowing that he would be cast into the lions' den.

"Daniel," said King Darius, "your God whom you serve so faithfully—surely He will deliver you."

Then the servants took Daniel away and threw him into the pit. They rolled the stone over the top and sealed it so that no one could try to help Daniel escape.

King Darius couldn't eat or sleep that night. He sent all his musicians away. He tossed and turned on his bed, hoping that Daniel's God would deliver him.

As soon as the first light of dawn peeked through the window, the king ran to the den of lions. Calling his servants, he commanded them to remove the stone. Then the king stepped to the edge of the pit and peered into the darkness.

"Oh, Daniel!" he cried, almost in tears. "Oh, Daniel, servant of the living God, was your God able to deliver you from the lions?"

From out of the darkness came a voice. "O King, live forever." It was the voice of Daniel! "My God sent His angel to shut the lions' mouths. They have not hurt me."

Oh, how happy King Darius was then! "Take Daniel out of the den of lions!" he shouted to his servants.

So Daniel was brought up out of the hole without even a scratch on his body. God had protected him because Daniel believed in Him.

The princes could hardly believe that Daniel was alive. They were just about to complain when King Darius gave another command. "Throw these wicked men into the pit!" he shouted.

Was Daniel kept safe because the lions weren't hungry? No! When the princes were thrown in, the lions broke all their bones before the men even hit the bottom of the den.

Then King Darius made a new decree and sent it through all the kingdom: "In every part of my kingdom," he said, "men shall fear Daniel's God. He is the living God. He shall reign forever, and His kingdom shall never be destroyed. He works great miracles in all the earth. He is the God that delivered Daniel from the power of the lions!"

A Lamb's Tale

Rico shifted his shoeshine box from one hand to the other as he struggled up the steep slope. He stopped a moment to rest and looked back down the mountain. The town of Ayacucho stretched below, a great bulk of a town half-hidden in the shadows of the Peruvian mountains. Already lights were blinking on in the houses. "I'm going to be late," Rico thought, hurrying on. "But it has been a good day. There were many, many shoes to shine."

Coins clinked in his pocket as he scrambled over a large rock. Rico jumped down, holding the shoeshine box carefully. He reached the path to his house and began to run. Ahead of him the setting sun bathed his adobe house in gold and outlined the reed fence. Rico ran past the fence, shouting "Hello, hello," to the startled goat. He threw open the back door, calling "Mama, I'm home!"

"So I can hear." Señora Perez smiled, turning from the stove. She gave Rico a hug and said, "I'm glad you took the short cut up the mountain instead of taking the road. There have been many cars on the road today. Fast cars roaring past and leaving clouds of dust over everything!"

"I know. There were many tourists in town today," Rico replied. "Look, Mama." Grinning, Rico emptied his pockets onto the table. "And dust makes many shoes to shine."

"Ah, Rico," his mother said happily. "A good day, indeed. Your papa will be pleased. He will be home soon too. You go wash up, dusty one."

When Rico returned to the kitchen, cheeks red from scrubbing, Señora Perez was hurrying to open the door. Rico's father was outside, holding something in his arms. He turned sideways to ease himself and his burden into the narrow doorway.

"Oh, the poor thing," Rico's mother cried.

Then Rico was at her elbow, reaching out to touch the little limp head. "It's a lamb," he said softly. "It's a sick lamb!"

"Wherever did you get a lamb?" Señora Perez asked.

"One of Pablo's ewes had twins. This one was the weakest, and its mother would not feed it." Señor Perez looked at Rico. "It has pneumonia," he warned. "Like Pablo said, it probably won't live."

"I'll take care of it, Papa," Rico said eagerly. "I'm sure it will be okay."

Señor Perez handed his burden to Rico and shrugged his shoulders, looking at his wife. "Well, it might. Rico has wanted a pet so long, I thought perhaps we could try."

Señora Perez looked doubtful. "We don't have any medicine. Neither do we have any extra milk to feed him."

Rico's black eyes begged. "I'll give the lamb my share of the goat's milk. And I'll pray to the Lord. Since He gave me this little lamb, He will make it better."

His mother's face softened. "The Lord does wonderful things for us. Even now your father has work when others do not. Make a straw bed in the corner for your little lamb."

Rico laughed, his eyes shining. "*Gracias*, Mama, Papa, *gracias*!" It didn't take long to make a small bed of fresh-smelling straw in the corner. Then Rico gently laid the little lamb on top.

Señora Perez knelt beside them, holding out a bowl of milk. "I warmed it a little," she said. "He won't take cold milk."

"*Gracias*, Mama," Rico said, taking the bowl. Propping the lamb's head in his lap, he carefully spooned the milk into the lamb's mouth. The milk ran out the other side and dripped onto Rico's pants.

"Try this way," said Rico's father as he took a clean cloth and twisted it at the end. He dipped the end into the warm milk and put it into the lamb's mouth. Nothing happened. Again Señor Perez dipped the cloth into the warm milk and put it into the lamb's mouth. Rico waited, hardly daring to breathe. The lamb stirred. Rico's lips moved as he prayed silently for the lamb to take the milk. With a little whimper the lamb began to suck the cloth.

"It worked!" Rico exclaimed, reaching for the cloth. Señor and Señora Perez stood up, sighing with relief.

"He's a long way from being well," Rico's father said, "but it's a beginning."

That night Rico slept on the floor close to the little lamb. He really intended to stay awake all night, but the excitement of the day had been too tiring. He was still sleeping the next morning when a weak "baa, baa" sounded in his ear. Rico's eyes blinked open.

"You are better, little lamb," he said. "*Gracias*, Lord, *gracias!*"

For a while he cuddled the lamb in his arms, stroking its soft wool. The lamb nuzzled closer, seeking its morning meal. Rico laughed and rolled to his feet. "Warm milk is what you need, all right. You'll eat and get well."

Though the lamb had begun to eat, it was still many days before it was well enough to go outside. Then Rico carried it out into the sunshine. The lamb lay in the grass as Rico hoed the potatoes. It curled up in the straw as Rico milked the goat, looking up to bleat softly when Rico was finished.

"Now, I can't carry you and the milk," Rico laughed as the little lamb nudged his legs. "Besides, you would have your nose in the pail in no time, greedy one."

"Baa," the lamb bleated as if in agreement. Rico started for the kitchen, and the lamb followed on shaky legs.

"Look, Mama," Rico called as his mother opened the door. "My lamb is walking all by himself!"

"And I thought he would never learn, the way you carry him everywhere," Señora Perez teased. "Yes, Rico, he does look fine now. He's a frisky little thing."

"Frisky!" Rico laughed as the lamb wobbled about, using his newly found freedom. "That's just the name for my lamb!"

And frisky he was. "Baa, baa," the lamb said when he knocked over Señora Perez's corn pot. She just shook her head when the lamb looked up at her with big brown eyes.

"Baa, baa," Frisky said when he brushed against Señora Perez's woodpile and sent the twigs scattering. And curious! Frisky wanted to know about everything and everybody. Rico couldn't stop laughing when Frisky got his nose stuck in an empty flowerpot. Trying to get the pot off, the lamb backed into the washpot and sent it clattering. "It's a good thing that washpot was empty, too," Señora Perez scolded as Rico removed the flowerpot.

Frisky cuddled up to Rico as if he knew he was in trouble again. Rico ran his fingers through the lamb's wool. "My little lamb will give us fine thick wool, Mama. Then you will have a new skirt, and Father and I will have new sweaters."

His mother smiled. "Now Rico—all from this pesky little lamb?" But she touched the patches on her worn skirt and said no more about the washpot.

Frisky trotted after Rico everywhere he went. Out to milk the goat, down to hoe the potatoes, wherever Rico was, there was Frisky.

"You will need to put him inside the fence soon," Señora Perez warned. "He will follow you to the road one day."

"I try to stay away from the road." Rico looked across the field to the road that curved around the mountain. "So many people take the road over the mountains to see the Inca ruins. But it is good for business. Last Saturday was another good day to shine shoes."

Señor Perez nodded. "I have been thinking of putting a stand beside the road to sell vegetables. And your mother would like to sell some of her rugs."

"The tourists would stop to buy them!" Rico said. "It is a good idea."

"We will have to put Frisky into the pen with the goat," his father said. "He will be happy there."

But Frisky was not happy in the pen. He bleated and bleated. Any time someone opened the gate, he pushed past and rushed out. Rico always chased him until the lamb was tired. Then he put Frisky back into the pen.

Señora Perez shook her head. "One day he's going to get out when you're gone. I'll never catch him!"

"Maybe Papa will be here," Rico said. "I'm only gone on Saturdays, and the stand is almost finished. Papa said he would be here every Saturday to help you at the stand."

His mother nodded. "The stand should be finished this Saturday. If business goes well, maybe you won't have to go to Ayacucho any more. Or maybe," she said thoughtfully, "we can all go and have our own stall in the marketplace."

The next Saturday Rico left early. He hurried down the mountain trail, eager to be at the bottom before the red sun spread out her warm blanket for the day.

"If I work hard enough today," Rico thought, "maybe I can leave early. Then I could help Mama and Papa at the stand."

When Rico reached town, he quickly picked out the best spot and waited. Soon the streets were full of people, going in and out of the stores. "Shine your shoes?" Rico called. "Shoes shined!"

Right from the beginning, business was good. Rico shined black shoes, brown shoes, and tan shoes. There were even a few pairs of dark purple shoes and white shoes to shine. Hour after hour he worked; the thought of going home early made him forget his aching shoulders and sore fingers.

At last, though, Rico could work no longer. It seemed as if every muscle in his body decided to complain at once. After putting away his shoeshine tools and picking up the box, he walked wearily out of town and began the long walk home.

Up the trail he climbed, turning off onto the path leading home. He stopped at the fence to say hello to Frisky, then went into the kitchen to leave his shoeshine box. Out again, he called to the bleating Frisky, "Be good, Frisky. I'll be back soon." Rico hurried down to the road without hearing the thumps as Frisky bumped against the gate, trying to get out.

Señor and Señora Perez looked up with surprise as Rico rounded the corner of the brightly painted stand. "Business was good in town," Rico explained, handing his father the coins. "How is it here?"

"Good," Señora Perez answered, showing Rico the few rugs she had left. "Many people on the way home from the ruins stopped to buy vegetables. And some bought my rugs!"

"It has gone well," Rico's father agreed. "But now it is time to close. Rico can help me pack the things up while you go milk the goat."

Happily, Señora Perez walked up the path to the house, counting the coins as she went. Rico and his father began to pack the vegetables onto the cart. "We can store them in the shed until tomorrow," Señor Perez said, raising his voice as another car whizzed past them.

"There are still people on the road. Why not wait a while?" Rico asked.

"The sun is beginning to go down," his father replied. "When the cars come around the bend, the people do not see us soon enough to stop.

You and your mother can open the stand Monday when I am at work."

Rico had lifted the last box when he heard a cry from the house. He looked up. Frisky was running down the path with Señora Perez behind him.

"Catch him!" she called. Rico ran to turn Frisky back toward the house, but the lamb whisked past him.

"No, Frisky," Rico called. "Stay out of the road!"

He started after the lamb, but his father stopped him. "Wait, he'll just run away," Señor Perez said. "Frisky doesn't want to be caught. You go around that way, and I'll try to send him toward you."

Rico moved to the left, talking softly to the lamb. But Frisky, watching Señor Perez, merely flicked his tail. Then he charged straight at the road.

"Come back!" Rico cried.

A big car roared around the bend and swept past them in a cloud of dust. Rico ran for the road. At the edge Frisky lay sprawled in the settling dust.

"Frisky's hurt," Rico sobbed as his parents hurried over. Señor Perez leaned over the motionless lamb.

"He'll be all right, won't he, Papa?" Rico's voice trembled. "Just like the time he got well when we didn't think he would. You remember, Mama? Nobody thought he would get well but he did, didn't he? Didn't he?"

Señora Perez wiped her eyes with her apron and put her arms around Rico. She looked helplessly at Señor Perez. Rico's father shook his head. "I'm afraid not, Rico, not this time."

"But the Lord healed him last time. The Lord gave him to me and healed him, and the Lord can do it again. I know it!"

"It's different this time, Rico." Señor Perez spoke slowly. "Last time Frisky was only sick." He hesitated a minute, and Rico looked up.

Finally Señor Perez said quietly, "Frisky is dead, son. Why don't you go to the house with your mother?"

For a while there were only the sounds of Rico's crying and his mother's murmurs as she comforted him. Then Rico looked up at his father, tears still flowing. "I want to help take care of Frisky," Rico said, standing up. "I want him to be under the big tree down by the field."

A week later Señora Perez looked out the window and saw Rico crossing the field to the big tree. "There he goes again," she sighed. "I wish I had never gone to milk the goat that evening. Maybe Frisky would still be alive today."

Señor Perez came to stand beside her. "No, it could have happened anytime. Don't worry yourself so. Frisky would have found another way to get out."

"Rico misses him so," she whispered. "I wish I could bear his pain for him."

"Time will erase much of the pain, and Rico will have good memories of Frisky," Señor Perez said. "But it will take time. When I was a child, I had a dog . . . " He stopped and reached for his hat. "I'll go talk to the boy."

Señora Perez watched as her husband walked across the field. When he reached the big tree, she saw him reach out to touch Rico's shoulder. They stood together, two dark shadows under the branches of the tree. The señora turned away from the window and sighed. "Time," she thought. "Yes, it will take time."

A Curtain of Spun Silver

(a true story)

Mr. Havers bowed to pray in the rustic chapel. The men, women, and children knelt on the rough wooden floor and joined him.

They prayed for Archbishop Sheldon, who persecuted the little church and tried to imprison Mr. Havers. They prayed for the families of the ten men who had been arrested and might be put to death. Finally, they thanked God for His loving protection and care and for the salvation He gave in Christ Jesus.

Mr. Havers hummed the closing hymn thoughtfully as the congregation rose to leave.

Two strong men slowly lowered the chains of the drawbridge. They crossed the deep, water-filled moat and searched for soldiers that might be hiding by the road. At last the men motioned for the others to cross. Silently the congregation hurried to their cottages in the nearby villages.

At home Mr. Havers opened his Bible and started to study. A loud knocking came from the door. Mr. Havers rose and opened the peephole. A young boy stood gasping for breath, his cheeks bright red and fear in his eyes.

"What troubleth thee?" Mr. Havers asked, lifting the latch.

"The men who work for Archbishop Sheldon just rode through the village. They seek thy life." The boy held his side. "Flee, Mr. Havers. They are hardhearted and will not let you live to be tried fairly."

Mr. Havers glanced toward the village. A cloud of dust rose above the thatched roofs.

"See, their horses approach even now," the boy said. "Oh, please flee, Mr. Havers." The boy turned and raced to the gate.

"Trust God," Mr. Havers called in his strong, deep voice. "He shall protect us both."

He slipped his Bible into his inside pocket, closed the door, and dashed into the woods. Hooves thundered past him on the road. Out of sight, he ran toward the mill. As he crossed an open field, he heard a cry go up from the far road. The horsemen had reached the empty house.

Mr. Havers dared run no farther. Finding the house empty, the men would search the woods and fields.

He slipped into a malt house, searching for a place to hide. Only an empty kiln seemed big enough to crawl inside. Mr. Havers slid as far as possible into the dark shadows, but the sunlight poured in through an open window and lit up the doorway of the kiln.

As he lay curled up on the brick floor, panting for breath, a spider dropped across the doorway, trailing a long thread behind her. Back and forth the spider swung, attaching her silk to the top and sides in wider and wider circles.

The long strands soon covered the door of the kiln in a beautiful design. The web glistened like spun silver in the light from the window.

Suddenly the door of the malt house burst open. Heavy boots tramped across the floor. Mr. Havers held his breath. He had forgotten he was hiding as he watched the spider.

"He must be in here. I'll break his head when I catch him, I will," a gruff voice said.

The steps moved closer to the kiln. "It's no use to look in there. The old villain can never be there. Look at that spider's web. He could never have gotten in there without breaking it."

"Come on, then. He must have escaped through the woods," the first voice said.

The door closed. Mr. Havers waited until all was quiet. "A curtain of spun silver to hide me," he murmured, slipping through the spider web and escaping to safety. He paused briefly to thank the Lord for His protection brought about by a little spider and her web.

THE MASTER WEAVERS

Have you ever wondered how a spider dashes up and down its sticky web and never tangles its own eight legs into a terrible knot? Most spiders have about six spinnerets which produce thread for making webs. Each spinneret spins a different kind of thread, some sticky and some nonsticky. Each of the threads is very strong, even though it is thinner than a strand of your hair. In fact, you would have to pile a million of the threads on top of each other to make a one-inch-high stack!

The thread is stronger than your hair, too. The faster a spider lets out its thread, the stronger the thread is.

When the spider weaves a web, it first anchors the web in place then uses nonsticky thread for lines and cables. Each thread is kept in place with a sticky attachment disk of tiny loops, each smaller than a dandelion seed.

Once the lines are in place, the little weaver sets its trap. First it spins a nonsticky thread around the lines and cables in smaller and smaller spirals.

When it reaches the middle of the web, it scurries back to the beginning of the spiral and picks up the nonsticky thread as it spins a sticky insect-catching thread in its place.

Around and around it travels until it reaches the middle a second time. Then the spider crawls off to hide, stepping only on the lines and not the sticky spiral.

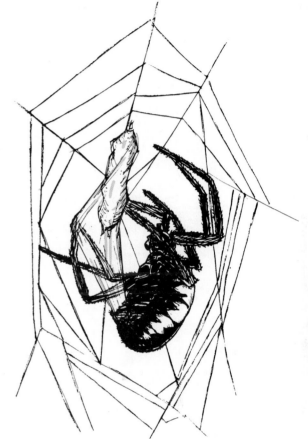

Even the slightest quiver of a trapped bug sends the spider racing across the lines to wrap up its victim in a thick band of thread.

Spiders eat many insects which bother man. God may have created these master weavers for that purpose. The next time you discover a spider, you may want to watch it spin its web yourself.

Under the Tent of the Sky

The wind cracked his whip,
The storm flashed a gun,
And the animal-clouds marched one by one
Under the tent of the sky.

There were elephants, blue,
And shaggy white bears,
And dozens and dozens of prancing gray mares
With their beautiful heads held high.

There were soft-footed panthers
And ostriches, fluffy,
And a great hippopotamus, purple and puffy,
Who wallowed in mud-colored mist.

There were small curly dogs
And camels with humps
And a wrinkled rhinoceros, all over bumps,
With a horn as big as your fist.

There was even a lion
Bedecked with a mane
Who growled so loud that he turned into rain
And tumbled to earth with a sigh.

The wind cracked his whip
And out came the sun
And the animal-clouds passed one by one
Out of the tent of the sky.

Rowena Bastin Bennett

What About Dolphins?

The dolphin isn't an ordinary fish. In fact, the dolphin isn't a fish at all—it's a mammal. That means it has to breathe air just the way you and I do. The dolphin's "nose" is on top of its head, like a whale's. It can close its "nose" while it swims underwater, but it has to get back to the surface every few minutes to take another breath.

Dolphins almost always travel in groups, called schools. Not only do they play games together—games like catch and tag—but they also help take care of each other. If a dolphin is hurt and can't get to the surface of the water to breathe, another dolphin will push it up to the surface and hold it there. The members of the school also protect each other from enemies, such as sharks.

If a shark sees a baby dolphin, he'll often try to kill it. The baby dolphin looks like a good meal for the shark until all the dolphin family attacks. With their powerful snouts they'll ram the shark's side again and again. Dolphins can usually kill an attacking shark.

Why is all this important to man? Even though dolphins can kill a shark, they won't attack people, even the people who capture or hurt them. Why not? No one knows. But there are even stories of dolphins' saving the lives of drowning swimmers. There's no other wild animal that's as friendly to man as the dolphin.

This friendliness aroused people's interest in finding out more about dolphins. When Marineland opened in Florida in 1938, strange and beautiful fish were the main attraction. Later the owners added a few dolphins. Before long the dolphins became the main attraction! Squeaking and rasping, these friendly creatures stuck their heads out of the water and tossed sea shells to the spectators. If someone threw a ball into their tank, the dolphins threw it back. The people, enjoying the dolphins' playfulness, went back to Marineland again and again just to see the dolphins.

Soon men found that these clever creatures could do a few tricks on their own. Trainers found ways to teach dolphins new and more complicated tricks. Some dolphins learned to play basketball, rise up on their tails in the water, and jump up twenty feet to ring a bell. The dolphins seemed to love to learn and to be with the people who taught them.

Before long scientists became interested in dolphins. By testing these creatures, they found dolphins to be one of the most intelligent kinds of animals on earth. Scientists learned that the dolphin could move very fast underwater, much faster than ships. Scientists also learned that the dolphin could come up from deep water quickly without getting sick the way divers do. Finally, they found that a dolphin could find objects underwater very easily with a system called *sonar*.

A dolphin's sonar helps him "see" objects with his ears, even in the muddiest water. By making clicking noises and listening to the echoes, he can tell how far away an object is, how big it is, and even what kind of material it is made of. A sonar device on one of our ships isn't nearly as good as a dolphin's. The dolphin can tell the difference between two different kinds of little fish, but with our sonar, men sometimes can't tell the difference between a ship and a whale! Scientists are working hard to learn all that they can from this marvelous system the Lord gave to dolphins.

Dolphins are now being used in other kinds of experiments too. Scientists are studying the way dolphins seem to be able to communicate with each other. Sometimes divers take dolphins to the bottom of the ocean for guides and for protection from sharks. The Navy uses dolphins to help transport materials from one place to another.

Maybe someday you'll read about dolphins' helping to find ships that have been buried underwater for many years. Or maybe in the future you'll see a dolphin lifeguard swimming near a beach, trained to rescue drowning swimmers. One thing, though, is certain. The dolphin is one of God's creatures that is not only very intelligent but also fun to watch!

Fremont's Frog Farm

It isn't easy to make money, as Monty Brown finds out. A few frogs seem to have a way of getting out of hand, and Monty's longed-for baseball mitt seems farther and farther away.

A Better Way Than Lemonade

Monty looked at his watch: five o'clock. He looked at the three piles of coins in front of him and sighed. The big pile of coins went to his mother for lemons and sugar. The middle-sized pile of coins went to his father for paper cups. And the small pile was his. He sighed again. One dollar and twenty-three cents surely wasn't enough to buy the baseball mitt in Mr. White's window. There had to be a better way to earn money than by selling lemonade.

Monty poured himself the last cup of lemonade. Then he went over to the lilac bush in front of the house and pulled out the paper the newsboy had thrown there. Daydreaming, he flipped page after page.

"Hey, look at that! There's a restaurant on Long Island that serves frog legs." Monty read the menu out loud. "Fried frog legs—delicious, delectable, and tasty." He continued flipping through the paper, still daydreaming.

"Fremont! Fremont Brown!" Mother stood at the back door calling her son for dinner.

"That's it!" yelled Monty, jumping up and snapping his fingers. "I'll go into business selling frogs!" He headed toward the back door. "Coming!"

That night Monty lay listening to the heavy rat-a-tat-tat of rain on the roof and wiggled with delight. "There'll be billions and trillions of frogs waiting for me in the morning. I sure am glad I got permission to go to the lake."

The next morning Monty woke before it was light, slipped into his clothes, and ate a bowl of cereal. Then he found his fishing net, put the net in his bike basket, and rode off to Catfish Lake.

Early morning mist drifted over the cattails as Monty walked carefully along the edge of the water.

"There's one!" he whispered, plunging his net into the water. "Missed him," he muttered. He stood still, listening and watching. Suddenly he thrust his net down into the water again. This time he got his prize.

"Aha!" said Monty to the frog. "You are the first frog in my new business. But what shall I do with you 'til I'm ready to go home?"

The frog just stared at him with big, dark eyes.

Monty hunted around until he found a box left by careless picnickers.

"This will do," he said, plopping the frog inside.

For the next two hours Monty slipped and slid along the muddy bank, thrusting his net in and out of the water. Sometimes he got a frog. Sometimes he didn't. At last, with his arm aching and his pantlegs dripping, Monty pedaled off toward home. The five frogs inside the box bumped and thumped.

Monty's mother took one look at his squishing sneakers sloshing muddy water on the clean floor and exclaimed, "Fremont Preston Brown! What have you been doing?" Her eyes traveled from the squishing sneakers up to the cardboard box thumping in Monty's hands.

Thump, thump, thump!

"It's alive! Get it out of here!" screamed thirteen-year-old Patti Ann. Monty frowned at her. Heavy footsteps behind him signaled that Dad had just arrived at the kitchen door. "What's going on here, son?"

Monty gulped. He had to make Dad understand. "I can't make enough money selling lemonade, so I'm going to raise frogs and sell them to restaurants for the most delicious, delectable, and tasty treat they've ever had on their menus. Please, Dad, let me do it. Patti Ann had goldfish in her room once."

This time Patti Ann frowned at Monty.

"That's true," Dad said slowly. "And I once had a friend who raised mice in his bedroom. Today he's a successful scientist. All right, son, you may raise frogs if you keep them in your own room in Patti Ann's old fish bowl."

"Thanks, Dad!" Monty disappeared upstairs while the box went thump, thump, thump at his every step.

Now it wasn't that the frogs multiplied until it cost Monty more than his allowance to buy dried flies for them to eat; or that every bucket, pan, waste basket, or jar disappeared into Monty's room; or that Monty spent all his time building moss-lined boxes for new frogs; or that Patti Ann found a frog in the bathtub one morning and screamed for fifteen minutes. No, none of these things was what made Dad finally lose his patience and decide he didn't want his son to be a scientist. It was the noise!

"Son," Dad said one morning, wiping his eyes while stifling a yawn. "Those frogs kept me awake all night!"

Monty squirmed in his seat. "I've kind of gotten used to them."

"But I haven't!" put in Patti Ann quickly.

"And what about the baseball mitt you wanted to buy?" reminded Mother.

"Son! Those frogs have got to go!" And by the way Dad raised his bushy eyebrows and squared his jaw, Monty knew he meant business.

The Restaurant Business

Monty paced back and forth in front of the house. Sometimes he ran to the gate and looked down the street. But it was while he was getting a drink of water in the house that the *Shelbyville News* arrived. Thud!

Monty made a dive under the porch and pulled out the paper. With his heart pounding, he turned to the last page.

"There it is!" he yelled, running inside and waving the paper. "There's my ad!" He pointed to the tiny three-line ad while Mother and Patti Ann crowded around to see.

> Frogs for sale. Will make delicious, delectable, and tasty frog legs. 5 frogs for $1.00. Call 235-2335.

"The phone will start ringing off the hook."

Mother's mouth curved into a smile as she patted Monty's shoulder. "I hope so."

Monty sat down on the chair next to the phone with pencil and paper in his hands. "I'll just wait here and take orders."

By dinnertime Monty had used up all his paper.

"Those are good pictures, son," Dad said. "But how many orders did you get?"

"None." Monty shook his head. "Not a single one."

"Maybe Mr. Murphy down at the Country Kitchen will buy all your frogs," suggested Patti Ann hopefully.

Monty's eyes lit up. "I'll go there first thing tomorrow!"

The next morning Monty paused in front of the restaurant window and studied himself. Balancing his box on one hand, he tucked in his shirt with the other and then pushed open the door to the restaurant.

Thump, thump, thump. Monty clutched the box more tightly as he wound his way among the tables of chattering people to the counter at the back. He climbed up on a stool and waited until Mr. Murphy finished serving a stranger.

"Howdy, Mr. Murphy. I've heard that you've got the best restaurant in town."

Mr. Murphy laughed. "Thanks, Monty. I've got the only restaurant in town."

Monty was glad to see Mr. Murphy in good humor. He plunged into his speech. "Would you like to buy some frogs for your restaurant? Frog legs are delicious, delectable, and tasty. The frogs only cost twenty cents apiece. I raise them myself and could bring them right to your door every week. The fresher the better, you know."

Mr. Murphy stood with his chin in his hand and his eyes focused on the ceiling. At last he shook his head. "Nope, it wouldn't work. My wife's the cook around here, and she hates frogs."

Monty's face fell.

"But," added Mr. Murphy in haste, "I'm sure you've got nice frogs. Maybe you could advertise in the paper."

"I already did." Monty sighed. "Nobody called."

"Excuse me, sonny." The stranger at the counter tapped Monty's shoulder. "May I take a look at your frogs?"

Monty pried open one corner of the box, and the stranger bent over to look.

Thump, thump, thump. All of the frogs jumped at once for the small corner of light.

Backward fell the stranger, up into the air went the box, and out came the frogs.

"Eeeeeee!" screamed the ladies, throwing down their sandwiches.

"Oh, no!" yelled Mr. Murphy, waving his towel in the air.

"I'll get them! I'll get them!" shouted Monty, diving under tables and scrambling over chairs.

Half an hour later Monty backed out the door while the box went thump, thump, thump in his hands. Mr. Murphy was still busy trying to quiet the ladies' jangled nerves, and the stranger was on his hands and knees looking for the last frog.

At the corner drug store, Monty sat down on the step to think. Plop! The newsboy threw the daily paper down next to him.

"Take it inside, will you?" he yelled, pedaling on.

Monty picked up the paper and looked at the headline.

Scientist Looks for Nonchemical
Means to Kill Flies

"We don't have any flies around our house, that's for sure." A half grin appeared on Monty's face; then it erupted into a full-blown shout. "That's it! I'll sell my frogs to the neighbors as flycatchers!"

281

It's Happened Before

As Monty hurried down the street, his heart thumped double time to the thump, thump, thump of the frogs in the box.

"This is it," he thought as he knocked on the first door. "I'll sell hundreds and thousands of frogs."

"Yes?" The lady's brief question let Monty know she was in a hurry.

"Would you like to buy a frog to catch your flies?"

"I don't catch flies. I swat them. Good day!"

Monty escaped to the next house with the echoing sound of the slammed door behind him.

"Howdy, Grandma Bell. Nice day, isn't it?" Monty eyed the fly swatter in her hand.

"It would be without these pesky flies."

Her rocking chair squeaked as she reached to swat at one. "Seems like they know I can't move around to get them. They stay just out of my reach."

"I've got just the thing you need." Monty groped around in his box and pulled out a plump green frog. "He'll catch all your flies."

"Well, looky there." Grandma peered over her glasses.

"I'm selling frogs," said Monty, "to earn money to buy a new mitt."

"Every boy needs a good baseball mitt. Just sell me two of those frogs, Monty."

"Thanks, Grandma! If you ever need any more, just give me a call." Monty put the coins in his pocket, picked up his thumping box, and went whistling down the street.

Four hours later Monty limped into his yard, the blisters on his feet throbbing with every step.

"Fremont, is that you?" Mother called from the kitchen. "It's five o'clock. Company will be here for dinner in just a few minutes. Go clean up quickly."

Monty put his box down, limped to his room, and emptied his pockets.

"Ten, twenty, thirty . . ." Monty counted his dimes, dividing them into piles. "One dollar goes to Dad for the newspaper ad. Fifty cents belongs to Mother for frog food. And the rest is mine." Monty sighed. "One dollar and seventy cents. I'll never get that new mitt in Mr. White's window."

B-r-r-ing. Monty could tell by the excited helloes out in the hall that company had arrived. He hurried to get dressed.

"Eeeee! There's a frog on the table!"

Monty knew his sister's squeal by now. He dashed past the company into the dining room where Patti Ann was jumping around like one of his frogs.

"I'll get it! I'll get it!" he cried, diving under the table.

Laughter came from the hall where the company stood. "Seems to me as if I've seen this happen before!"

Monty's ears burned. He had heard that voice before! He backed out from under the table, clutching the frog in his left hand. There in the dining room stood the stranger from the Country Kitchen.

"Monty," Dad said, "I'd like you to meet an old friend of mine, Dr. Smelzer."

The stranger, who was not a stranger anymore
but Dr. Smelzer, laughed again and slapped
Monty on the back.

"I used to raise mice when I was a boy. No
money in that." He winked at Monty. "But now,
frogs . . . there might be a lot of money in frogs."

"Nope," said Monty, "not much. Nobody
around here wants to buy frogs."

"I do."

"You do?" Monty's eyes opened wide. "What for?"

Dr. Smelzer looked this way and that, then
cupped his hand to his mouth and whispered,
"Frogs eat flies."

Suddenly something clicked in Monty's mind.
"You're the scientist I read about in the
newspaper. And you want my frogs to get rid of
all those flies so you don't have to use chemicals.
Wowee!"

When Dr. Smelzer left that night, he handed
Monty a check. "My men will be by tomorrow to
get your frogs. Just make sure they're hungry."

"Yes, sir!" said Monty, grinning. "Hey Dad,
maybe we can have our own pond. We'll put out
a sign that reads 'Fremont's Frog Farm' . . . ."

"Oh, no," groaned Mother.

"Eeeee!" screamed Patti Ann.

" . . . and raise billions and trillions of frogs,"
continued Monty, still daydreaming.

The Dog and the Meat

One day a burly brown dog bounded through town, carrying a juicy hunk of meat. As he ran over the wooden bridge that lay across the river leading home, the dog glanced into the water. On the smooth surface of the river he saw a stout brown dog with a piece of meat hanging from its mouth. The burly brown dog bristled. The other dog bristled. He growled deep in his throat. The other dog stood as silent as stone.

"Give me your meat!" the burly brown dog snarled. But as he opened his mouth to bark, his meat fell with a splash, making the reflection of himself ripple into little waves that raced to the shore. The meat disappeared into the murky depths, and all that the burly brown dog could do was bark at his own reflection.

Moral: Greediness may cause one to lose everything.

Forgiven

I found a little beetle, so that Beetle was his name,
And I called him Alexander and he answered just the same.
I put him in a match-box, and I kept him all the day . . .
And Nanny let my beetle out—
    Yes, Nanny let my beetle out—
    She went and let my beetle out—
    And Beetle ran away.

She said she didn't mean it, and I never said she did,
She said she wanted matches and she just took off the lid,
She said that she was sorry, but it's difficult to catch
An excited sort of beetle you've mistaken for a match.

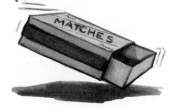

She said that she was sorry, and I really mustn't
   mind,
As there's lots and lots of beetles which she's
   certain we could find
If we looked about the garden for the holes where
   beetles hid—
And we'd get another match-box and write
   BEETLE on the lid.

We went to all the places which a beetle might be
   near,
And we made the sort of noises which a beetle
   likes to hear,
And I saw a kind of something, and I gave a
   sort of shout:
"A beetle-house and Alexander Beetle coming out!"

It was Alexander Beetle I'm as certain as can be
And he had a sort of look as if he thought it
    must be ME,
And he had a sort of look as if he thought he
    ought to say:
"I'm very very sorry that I tried to run away."

And Nanny's very sorry too for
    you-know-what-she-did,
And she's writing ALEXANDER very blackly on
    the lid.
So Nan and Me are friends, because it's difficult
    to catch
An excited Alexander you've mistaken for a
    match.

A. A. Milne

A Gift for Uncle Tom

It seemed as if everyone in Toby Johnson's house was doing something important to get ready for Uncle Tom's visit. Everyone, that is, except Toby. Toby's efforts to help only led to trouble and more trouble.

The Big Catch

Toby ran up a few steps, turned around, and took a flying leap, at the same time throwing his rag at the chandelier hanging from the fourteen-foot ceiling.

"Mercy! Mercy!" yelled Liza, who had just come around the corner with her arms full. Up into the air flew blankets, sheets, and pillows. Down on the floor tumbled the black servant and the nine-year-old boy.

"Ah-choo!" sneezed Toby. Duck feathers from a torn pillow floated through the air. "Ah-choo! Ah-choo!"

"Tobias Lee Johnson! What is going on here?" From beneath the blankets Toby could hear

Mother's long skirts swishing angrily. He lifted one
corner of the blue blanket draped over his head
and peeped out. His mother stood in the doorway
with her hands on her hips, the lace on her cap
bouncing up and down.

"Get out from under those blankets," Mother
ordered, at the same time turning to help Liza,

who was still thrashing around somewhere underneath the piles of bedding.

Toby scrambled out and began hurriedly gathering up blankets, sheets, and pillows. "Ah-choo! Ah-choo! Ah-choo!"

By this time Mother had Liza, who was gasping for breath, on her feet.

"Never mind the bedding, Toby."

Toby dropped his armful to the floor, sending up another shower of feathers.

"What *were* you doing?"

"I was just trying to help," began Toby, looking at Mother's face and figuring he had better talk quickly. "I heard you say that the chandelier needed dusting, and I couldn't reach it by standing on a chair. I thought I could knock the dust off with my rag."

Mother shook her head while Liza turned her broad back to stifle a laugh. "Toby, Toby, sometimes you are too helpful. Impulsive, I think your father would say. Well, thank you for your help, but run along. There's too much to do before your Uncle Tom arrives this afternoon. You'll just have to spend the morning outside." She pointed to the door. "Now go, and make sure you're back for the special church meeting. You know Uncle Tom is going to be the preacher."

Under protest Toby backed out the door. Sighing, he wandered around to the back of the large brick house. It seemed as if everyone was getting ready for Uncle Tom's arrival—everyone, that is, except Toby. Mary was baking bread in the kitchen; Buck was almost finished polishing the carriage; and Benjamin had the horses looking sleek and shiny. It didn't matter where Toby offered his help; he was either too little, too late, or just plain in the way.

"I think I'll take a walk," Toby announced to no one in particular. He looked around, but everyone seemed too busy to notice him. Closing the front gate behind him, Toby started down the cobblestone street, slipping his hands into his pockets.

"Ouch!" he exclaimed, hastily pulling his right hand back out again. A fishing hook came with it, followed by ten feet of twisted string. Toby gingerly unhooked his finger and then slowly wound the string around the hook. Before he had finished the task, an idea had taken root in his mind.

"Uncle Tom loves fresh fish." Toby's feet were already heading in the direction of the river. "I'll catch him the biggest and best one he ever ate!"

Down King Street, around the corner onto Milk Street, past the butcher shop, the silversmith's, and the blacksmith's he hurried. At the baker's shop, Toby slowed down. The freshly iced hot cross buns in the window looked so tempting. Toby disappeared into the shop and was back out in a moment, stuffing a bun into his jacket pocket. Fishing just might be hard work!

A Gift for Uncle Tom   295

At the river Toby dug around in the dirt until he found some fat worms. They were squishy too, he discovered as he tried to get a worm rather than his finger on the hook.

"This one's for Uncle Tom," he whispered, throwing the hook with the fat worm into the water.

Nothing happened. Toby jiggled his fishing line. He pulled a little of the line out of the water. He sighed. The only ripples on the water came from his line. He then settled back to wait. For a long time Toby stared at the lacy pattern the leaves made overhead, thinking about Uncle Tom's visits. Working hard as a circuit-riding preacher, Uncle Tom usually held several special meetings at the church. Always, however, he managed to spend a little time alone with Toby. One time Uncle Tom took him to the fair. Another time they went fishing below the mill. And . . .

Toby sat up and looked at the water. Not even a nibble! Pulling the line out of the water, he baited his hook with a fatter worm. This time his line plopped right near a sunken log. Toby pulled the line up just a little. Suddenly something pulled back!

Either the fish that grabbed the fat worm was terribly strong, or the river's edge was awfully slippery. Within seconds Toby found himself sliding toward the cold water.

Mud spattered and water sprayed as Toby's heels caught on a tree root. His downward slide suddenly stopped. With a "heave-ho!" Toby yanked the string. The fish soared out of the water and landed on the bank behind him. Flipping and flopping, it started sliding down the muddy bank.

"Oh, no you don't!" With a lunge Toby fell on top of the fish, lying there until it stopped wriggling. Triumphantly he staggered to his feet, the fish in his arms and a grin on his face. "Wait until Uncle Tom sees this one!"

On the Way Home

It seemed as if Toby's feet barely touched the ground as he headed back home carrying Uncle Tom's fish. He was halfway through the town when he heard a sound behind him.

Toby turned his head. One black cat, two gray cats, and three little yellow kittens with their noses in the air were heading toward him like boys after their mother's freshly baked bread. Toby wrapped his arms more tightly about the fish.

"Go home!" he yelled, stamping his foot. The cats kept closing in.

"Shoo! Get away from here!"

The big black cat rubbed against Toby's legs while the gray cats mewed pitifully. They seemed to be terribly hungry.

Toby started to run. Uncle Tom's fish slipped from his grasp and slithered down the front of his jacket. Toby grabbed desperately, catching hold of its tail. A gray cat leaped for the fish and caught its sharp claws on the edge of Toby's jacket.

Clasping the fish as tightly as he could, Toby gave a hard jerk on his jacket. Toby heard a ripping sound as the cat fell to the road. He looked down. His pocket dangled by one corner. His hot cross bun lay icing-side-down in the dirt. The cats noticed the bun too. They began scratching and clawing as they pounced on the bun, battling for the food. Toby ran down the road, not daring to look back.

Ding, dong. Ding, dong.

Toby stopped short. The church bells—he had forgotten all about Uncle Tom's meeting! Toby gulped. What was he going to do with the fish? He didn't dare to be late for the meeting!

Toby glanced around. Outside the printer's shop lay a pile of old newspapers. Toby hurried over and quickly wrapped up his fish. Then he unbuttoned his muddy jacket, laid the fish against his chest, and buttoned his jacket again. The jacket fit so snugly that the fish couldn't possibly slip out.

Breathing a sigh of relief, Toby raced for the church. Just as the bells stopped pealing, Toby slipped inside and sat down in the last pew. The newspaper crinkled and crunched.

Toby tried to sit very still. It was awfully hot! As he moved to a more comfortable position, the papers crunched loudly.

The boy next to Toby leaned over and whispered, "Whatcha got in there, Toby?"

"Nothing."

The boy raised his eyebrows and gave Toby a dig with his elbow. "Sure you do. What is it?"

A man tapped the boys on the shoulders. "Shhh!"

By this time Toby could feel the dampness of the fish through the newspaper. He fanned himself, then sniffed. "Oh, no," he groaned to himself. "I can smell my fish!"

Uncle Tom got up to speak, but Toby didn't hear a word he said. The boy next to Toby began to giggle. Then Toby saw Mrs. Tarby's nose begin to twitch and the feathers on her hat begin to bob. She leaned over and whispered something to Mrs. Morgan. Mrs. Morgan sniffed the air, nodded, and leaned over to whisper to her oldest daughter. Up and down the pews closest to Toby, people whispered and sniffed. Toby watched miserably. Maybe this hadn't been such a good idea after all. At last Uncle Tom finished preaching and walked back to sit with Toby's mother and father. He winked at Toby before sitting down in the pew two rows up from Toby.

When the regular minister stood up to speak, it seemed to Toby that he was looking right at him.

The minister asked one of the men to dismiss the meeting and walked to the back of the church. Toby's feet twitched. Almost before the "Amen" sounded, Toby was out of the pew. He wasn't going to stand around for any questions. But at the door the minister's arm barred the way.

"Hold on, there, Tobias Lee!" he said, sniffing. "Just what do you have there?"

"J-just s-something for Uncle Tom," Toby stammered.

"For me?" said a voice.

Toby spun around, clutching his jacket.

There was Uncle Tom, a wide grin on his face. Mother and Father stood behind him. There were no grins on their faces as they looked at Toby's muddy clothes and torn jacket. Toby's heart sank.

Uncle Tom sniffed. "Why Toby, how thoughtful! You've remembered how much I like fish," he said, reaching into Toby's jacket and pulling out the wrapped fish. "Thank you!" He unwrapped part of the paper and smiled. "It's your favorite kind, Reverend."

"Why don't you join us for dinner, Reverend?" Mother said hastily, looking at the grinning crowd behind them. "We'll be glad to cook Toby's fish, and you can visit with Tom too."

"I'd be delighted, ma'am," replied the minister.

Toby let out a sigh of relief and followed Uncle Tom down the steps.

"What a fish, Toby!" exclaimed Uncle Tom. "How did you catch him?"

"Well," Toby beamed. "It's a long story. . . ."

GLOSSARY

This glossary has information about selected words found in this reader. You can find meanings of words as they are used in the stories. Certain unusual words such as foreign names are included so that you can pronounce them correctly when you read.

The pronunciation symbols below show how to pronounce each vowel and several of the less familiar consonants.

ă	pat	ĕ	pet	î	fierce
ā	pay	ē	be	ŏ	pot
â	care	ĭ	pit	ō	go
ä	father	ī	pie	ô	paw, for

oi	oil	ŭ	cut	zh	vision
o͝o	book	û	fur	ə	ago, item,
o͞o	boot	*th*	the		pencil, atom,
yo͞o	abuse	th	thin		circus
ou	out	hw	which	ər	butter

ac·knowl·edge | ăk nŏl′ ĭj | —*verb* To recognize the authority or position of.

ac·tu·al | ăk′ chōō əl | —*adj.* Existing in fact; real.

a·do·be | ə dō′ bē | —*noun* Brick or bricks made of clay and straw that dry and harden in the sun.

adobe

al·ley | ăl′ ē | —*noun* A narrow street or passage between or behind buildings.

am·bush | ăm′ bŏŏsh′ | —*verb* To attack from a hidden position.

am·mu·ni·tion | ăm′ yə nĭsh′ ən | —*noun* Bullets, explosives, bombs, or anything else that can be fired from a gun or weapon or can explode and cause damage.

an·chor | ăng′ kər | —*verb* To hold in place; fix firmly.

Ar·gen·ti·na | är jən tē′ nə | —*noun* A country in South America.

ar·mored car | är′ mərd kär | —*noun* A vehicle covered with armor or some strong material such as steel; used for transporting money and valuable goods.

armored car

a·rouse | ə rouz′ | —*verb* To stir up; excite.

Bab·y·lon | băb′ ə lən | or | băb′ ə lŏn′ | —*noun* A capital city east of Israel; in the Bible it is often a term used for evil or worldliness.

belfry

blacksmith

ă	pat	ĕ	pet
ā	pay	ē	be
â	care	ĭ	pit
ä	father	ī	pie
î	fierce	oi	oil
ŏ	pot	o͞o	book
ō	go	o͞o	boot
ô	paw,	yo͞o	abuse
	for	ou	out
ŭ	cut	zh	vision
û	fur	ə	ago, item,
th	the		pencil, atom,
th	thin		circus
hw	which	ər	butter

bale | bāl | —*noun* A large, tightly wrapped bundle of raw material.

band | bănd | —*noun* A strip of cloth or some other kind of material that binds or ties together.

bar·ri·cade | băr′ ĭ kād′ | or | băr ĭ kād′ | —*verb* To block off or prevent from moving.

bay | bā | —*adj.* Reddish brown.

bel·fry | bĕl′ frē | —*noun* A tower or steeple where bells are hung.

bind | bīnd | —*verb* To wrap a bandage around.

black·smith | blăk′ smĭth′ | —*noun* A person who makes things out of iron. A blacksmith heats the iron and shapes and hammers it into horseshoes, tools, and other objects.

Blue Ridge | blo͞o rĭj | —*noun* Eastern ranges of the Appalachian Mountains. From a distance, the peaks appear to be blue because of the forests on their slopes.

bon·dage | bŏn′ dĭj | —*noun* The condition of being a slave; slavery.

Boones·bor·ough | bo͞onz′ bôr ō | —*noun* A settlement in Kentucky founded by Daniel Boone.

Bos·ton Com·mon | bô′ stən | or | bŏs′ tən kŏm′ ən | —*noun* Fifty acres of land in the center of the old city of Boston. It is known as the oldest public park in the United States.

breed | brēd | —*noun* A particular type of animal that has been produced from a selected group of parents.

bulk | bŭlk | —*noun* The largest part of; greatest portion.

bur·ly | bûr′ lē | —*adj.* Heavy; strongly built; husky.

cane·brake | kān′ brāk′ | —*noun* A dense growth of cane.

cane stub·ble | kān stŭb′ əl | —*noun* Short, stiff stalks left after cane has been cut.

cat·e·chism | kăt′ ə kĭs′ əm | —*noun* A set of questions and answers used for teaching religious doctrine.

cat·tail | kăt′ tāl′ | —*noun* A tall plant that grows in wet places. It has long, narrow leaves and a long, dense cluster of tiny brown flowers.

cav·ern | kăv′ ərn | —*noun* A large cave.

chan·de·lier | shăn′ də lîr′ | —*noun* A light fixture with several arms or branches that hold light bulbs or candles. A chandelier hangs from the ceiling.

Cher·o·kee | chĕr′ ə kē′ | —*noun* A member of the Cherokee Indian tribe.

chief | chēf | —*noun* A person with the highest rank; a leader. —*adj.* 1. Highest in rank. 2. Most important; main.

chide | chīd | —*verb* To scold; rebuke; reprimand.

cir·cuit rid·er | sûr′ kĭt rīd′ ər | —*noun* A preacher who traveled from church to church in some areas of the country.

clam·my | klăm′ ē | —*adj.* Damp, sticky, and usually cold.

cattail

chandelier

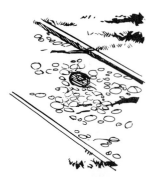

cobblestone

cockle

ă	pat	ĕ	pet
ā	pay	ē	be
â	care	ĭ	pit
ä	father	ī	pie
î	fierce	oi	oil
ŏ	pot	ŏŏ	book
ō	go	ōō	boot
ô	paw,	yōō	abuse
	for	ou	out
ŭ	cut	zh	vision
û	fur	ə	ago, item,
th	the		pencil, atom,
th	thin		circus
hw	which	ər	butter

clas·sics | **klăs′** ĭks | —*noun* The writings of ancient Greece and Rome.

cli·mate | **klī** mĭt | —*noun* The usual weather a place has all year, including its temperature, rainfall, and wind.

coax | kōks | —*verb* To try in a gentle or pleasant way to get a person or animal to do something.

cob·ble·stone | **kŏb′** əl stōn′ | —*noun* A round stone once used to cover streets.

coc·kle | **kŏk′** əl | —*noun* A small sea animal that has a pair of shells shaped something like a heart.

col·umn | **kŏl′** əm | —*noun* A long line of things or people following one behind the other.

com·mu·ni·cate | kə **myōō′** nĭ kāt′ | —*verb* To speak to; to pass along or exchange thoughts, ideas, or information.

com·pa·ny | **kŭm′** pə nē | —*noun* 1. A guest or guests. 2. A business; a firm.

com·pli·cat·ed | **kŏm′** plĭ kāt′ əd | —*adj.* Not easy to understand or do.

Con·fed·er·ate | kən **fĕd′** ər ĭt | —*noun* A person who supported the Confederacy, the group of eleven southern states that left the United States in 1860 and 1861.

con·fuse | kən **fyōōz′** | —*verb* To mix up; mislead.

con·gre·ga·tion | **kŏng′** grə **gā′** shən | —*noun* A group of people gathered together for religious worship.

coon·hound | **kōōn′** hound′ | —*noun* A dog used for hunting raccoons.

cor·al | kôr′ əl | or | kŏr′ əl | —*noun* A substance, as hard as stone, that is formed by the skeletons of tiny sea animals. Large groups of these animals form rounded or branching masses. Coral is often brightly colored.

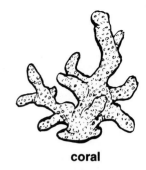

coral

cor·ri·dor | kôr′ ĭ dər | or | kôr′ ĭ dôr′ | or | kŏr′ ĭ dər | —*noun* A narrow hallway or passage with doors opening onto it.

coun·sel·or | koun′ sə lər | or | koun′ slər | —*noun* A person who advises or guides; adviser.

count·ess | koun′ tĭs | —*noun* 1. The wife of a count. 2. A woman with a rank equal to that of a count in her own right.

crock | krŏk | —*noun* An earthenware pot or jar.

crock

cuff | kŭf | —*verb* To strike with the open hand; slap; hit.

D

Da·ri·us | də rī′ əs | —*noun* A Median governor of Babylon.

de·lec·ta·ble | dĭ lĕk′ tə bəl | —*adj.* Very enjoyable; delightful; delicious.

den | dĕn | — *noun* The home or shelter of a wild animal; a lair.

de·pend·ent | dĭ pĕn′ dənt | —*adj.* Needing the help of someone or something else.

des·pair | dĭ spâr′ | —*noun* Lack of all hope.

de·vice | dĭ vīs′ | —*noun* Something that is made or used for a special purpose.

din·gy | dĭn′ jē | —*adj.* Dirty or soiled.

drawbridge

elk

disk | dĭsk | —*noun* A thin, flat, round object.

dou·ble back | dŭb′ əl băk | —*verb* To go back over the path one has just traveled.

draw·bridge | drô′ brĭj | — *noun* A bridge that can be raised or turned to prevent someone from crossing it.

drive | drīv | — *verb* To put into and keep in motion; move by force.

drought | drout | — *noun* A long period with little or no rain.

dry | drī | — *adj.* Humorous in a clever or sarcastic way.

dug·out | dŭg′ out′ | — *noun* A pit dug into the ground or on a hillside and used as a shelter.

ease | ēz | — *verb* To move slowly and carefully.

eel | ēl | — *noun* A long, slippery fish that looks like a snake.

el·der tree | ĕl′ dər trē | — *noun* A kind of shrub or small tree with clusters of small white flowers and bearing red or blackish berries.

elk | ĕlk | — *noun* A large deer of North America. The male has large, branching antlers.

e·rase | ĭ rās′ | — *verb* To remove all traces of.

es·cort | ĕs′ kôrt′ | — *noun* One or more guards, often armed, traveling with a prisoner or important person.

310

eve | ēv | — *noun* The evening or day before a special day.

e·vent | ĭ **vĕnt′** | —*noun* Something that happens; an occurrence.

ewe | yo͞o | — *noun* A female sheep.

ex·treme | ĭk **strēm′** | — *adj.* Very great or intense.

ewe

F

fend | fĕnd | —*verb* To turn away or aside; deflect.

fes·tiv·i·ty | fĕs **tĭv′** ə tē | — *noun* A feast or celebration of a special occasion.

fil·i·gree | **fĭl′** ə grē′ | — *adj.* Decoration made from gold, silver, or other fine twisted wire.

flank | flăngk | —*noun* The part between the hip and the ribs on either side of the body of an animal or person.

flush | flŭsh | — *adj.* A blush or rosy glow.

fo·cus | **fō′** kəs | — *verb* To adjust an instrument or the eyes so as to get a clear image.

for·ag·er | **fôr′** ĭj ər | —*noun* A raider who searches or hunts for food and supplies.

Frau | frou | —*noun* A German title for a married woman.

filigree

flank

G

gap | găp | —*noun* An opening, crack, or break.

ga·zette | gĭ zĕt′ | —*noun* A newspaper.

George III | jôrj | —*noun* King of Great Britain and Ireland during the American Revolution.

gin·ger·ly | jĭn′ jər lē | —*adv.* Carefully; delicately.

girth | gûrth | —*noun* A strap securing a saddle on an animal's back; a cinch.

gra·ci·as | grä′ sē äs | —The Spanish word for "thank you."

grade | grād | —*noun* A class or category; a type.

grav·el·ly | grăv′ əl lē | —*adj.* Having the quality of gravel; rough.

gust | gŭst | —*noun* A sudden, strong breeze.

girth

ham·mock | hăm′ ək | —*noun* A swinging bed made of rope or strong fabric and hung in the air between two supports.

hearth | härth | —*noun* The floor of a fireplace and the area around it.

heave | hēv | —*verb* To raise or lift with great effort.

herd | hûrd | —*verb* To gather, keep, or drive together.

her·i·tage | hĕr′ ĭ tĭj | —*noun* Something valuable to be used, shared, and preserved for future generations.

hes·i·tant | hĕz′ ĭ tənt | —*adj.* Stopping or waiting because one is not sure; doubtful.

hammock

ă	pat	ĕ	pet
ā	pay	ē	be
â	care	ĭ	pit
ä	father	ī	pie
î	fierce	oi	oil
ŏ	pot	ŏŏ	book
ō	go	ōō	boot
ô	paw,	yōō	abuse
	for	ou	out
ŭ	cut	zh	vision
û	fur	ə	ago, item,
th	the		pencil,atom,
th	thin		circus
hw	which	ər	butter

im·pris·on | ĭm prĭz′ ən | — *verb* To put in jail or prison; lock up.

im·pul·sive | ĭm pŭl′ sĭv | — *adj.* Inclined to act on a sudden urge, desire, or whim.

In·ca | ĭng′ kə | — *noun* A group of South American Indians who ruled Peru before the Spanish conquest.

in·flu·ence | ĭn′ floo əns | — *noun* The ability or power to change or have an effect on things.

in·ter·fere | ĭn′ tər fîr′ | — *verb* To get in the way of; interrupt; hinder.

Inca

jan·gled | jăng′ gəld | — *adj.* Grated on; jarred.

kiln | kĭl | or | kĭln | — *noun* An oven or furnace used for hardening, drying, or burning such things as grain and lumber.

kith and kin | kĭth ănd kĭn | — *noun* Friends, neighbors, and relatives.

kiln

la·bored | lā′ bərd | — *adj.* Done with hard work or great difficulty.

lilac

loft

leg·end | lĕj′ ənd | —*noun* A story that has been handed down from earlier times. It is usually not certain whether a legend is true or not.

li·lac | lī′ lək | or | lī′ lŏk′ | or | lī′ lăk | —*noun* A garden shrub with clusters of fragrant purplish or white flowers.

lodg·ing | lŏj′ ĭng | —*noun* A rented room or rooms.

loft | lŏft | —*noun* An open space under a roof; an attic.

loom | lo͞om | —*verb* To seem close at hand; be about to happen.

lux·u·ry | lŭg′ zhə rē | —*noun* Something that is not considered necessary but that gives great pleasure, enjoyment, or comfort. A luxury is usually something expensive or hard to get.

mam·mal | măm′ əl | —*noun* Any of a group of warm-blooded animals that have hair or fur on their bodies.

man·do·lin | măn′ dl ĭn′ | —*noun* A stringed musical instrument that has a pear-shaped body and a long neck.

mar·vel | mär′ vəl | —*verb* To be filled with wonder or admiration.

mast | măst | —*noun* A tall pole for the sails and rigging of a sailing ship.

Mar·ine·land | mə rēn′ lănd | —*noun* A tourist attraction featuring sea animals.

ă	pat	ĕ	pet
ā	pay	ē	be
â	care	ĭ	pit
ä	father	ī	pie
î	fierce	oi	oil
ŏ	pot	o͝o	book
ō	go	o͞o	boot
ô	paw,	yo͞o	abuse
	for	ou	out
ŭ	cut	zh	vision
û	fur	ə	ago, item,
th	the		pencil,atom,
th	thin		circus
hw	which	ər	butter

314

mate | māt | —*noun* An officer on a ship.

min·i | mĭn′ ē | —*adj.* Something especially smaller or shorter than usual.

min·i·a·ture | mĭn′ ē ə chər | —*adj.* Much smaller than the usual size.

mite | mīt | —*noun* A very small animal related to the spiders. Mites often live on plants or other animals.

moat | mōt | —*noun* A wide, deep ditch, usually filled with water. In the Middle Ages a moat was dug around castles and towns to protect them from enemies. A bridge could be lowered over the moat so people could cross over it.

moat

moc·ca·sin | mŏk′ ə sĭn | —*noun* A soft leather shoe, slipper, or low boot that does not have a heel. Moccasins were first worn by North American Indians.

mo·las·ses | mə lăs′ ĭz | —*noun* A thick, sweet syrup that is produced when sugar cane is made into sugar.

moccasin

moss | môs | or | mŏs | —*noun* One of a group of small green plants that do not have flowers. Moss often forms a covering on damp ground, rocks, or tree trunks.

murk·y | mûr′ kē | —*adj.* Dark and gloomy.

nar·row | năr′ ō | —*adj.* Small in width as compared to length; not wide. —*verb* Narrowed; narrowing; to make or become narrow or narrower.

ne·ces·si·ty | nə **sĕs′** ĭ tē | —*noun*
Something impossible to get along without; an essential.

no·bil·i·ty | nō **bĭl′** ĭ tē | —*noun* A social class having titles of rank and often wealth and power. Queens, kings, princes, and princesses are all part of the nobility.

non·chem·i·cal | **nŏn′** kĕm′ ĭ kəl | — *adj.*
Not involving the use of chemicals.

nudge | nŭj | —*verb* To poke or push in a gentle way.

oc·cu·pied | **ŏk′** yə pīd′ | —*adj.* Taken possession of and controlled by force; controlled.

ore | ôr | or | ər | —*noun* A mineral or rock that contains a valuable substance such as iron.

or·ner·y | **ôr′** nə rē | —*adj.* Stubborn; mean.

out·ly·ing | **out′** lī ĭng | — *adj.* Located at a distance from the center or the main part; far away.

pace | pās | —*noun* A step made in walking.

pains·tak·ing·ly | **pānz′** tā′ kĭng lē | —*adv.*
With great care; carefully.

parch·ment | **pärch′** mənt | —*noun* The skin of a sheep or goat, prepared as a material to write on.

parchment

par·lor | **pär′** lər | —*noun* A room for entertaining visitors.

par·tic·u·lar | pər **tĭk′** yə lər | —*adj.* Distinct from any other; certain; specific.

pas·sage | **păs′** ĭj | —*noun* A part of a written work or a piece of music.

pa·trol | pə **trol′** | —*verb* To go or walk through an area to guard it and make sure that there is no trouble.

pa·tron | **pā′** trən | —*noun* A person who regularly helps or supports a person or group by giving money.

per·se·cute | **pûr′** sĭ kyo͞ot′ | —*verb* To cause to suffer, especially because of political or religious beliefs.

Pe·ru | pə **ro͞o′** | —*noun* A country in South America.

Phil·a·del·phi·a | fĭl ə **dĕl′** fē ə | —*noun* A city in southeastern Pennsylvania.

pin·wheel | **pĭn′** hwēl′ | —*noun* A type of firework forming a spinning wheel of colored flames.

pinwheel

plan·ta·tion | plăn **tā′** shən | —*noun* A large farm or estate on which crops are grown and cared for by workers who also live on the farm. Cotton, sugar, tobacco, and rubber are among things grown on a plantation.

pneu·mo·nia | no͞o **mōn′** yə | or | nyo͞o **mōn′** yə | —*noun* A serious disease of the lungs.

porter

prow

pol·i·cy | **pŏl′** ĭ sē | —*noun* A belief or plan of action for doing something that is followed by a government, organization, group, or person.

por·ter | **pôr′** tər | —*noun* A person employed to carry goods or passengers.

po·si·tion | pə **zĭsh′** ən | —*noun* 1. The way a person or thing is placed or arranged. 2. Rank or status; job.

pov·er·ty | **pŏv′** ər tē | —*noun* The condition of being poor and having little money or other necessities.

prey | prā | —*noun* An animal hunted or caught by another animal for food.

prog·ress | **prŏg′** rĕs′ | —*noun* Forward movement.

prow | prou | —*noun* The pointed front part of a ship or boat; bow.

pub·li·ca·tion | pŭb lĭ **kā′** shən | —*noun* A book, magazine, newspaper, or other printed material that is published.

pulp | pŭlp | —*noun* The soft, juicy part of fruits and certain vegetables.

quill pen | kwĭl pĕn | —*noun* A writing pen that is made from a long, stiff feather.

ram | răm | —*verb* To crash or smash into.

ran·cid | **răn′** sĭd | —*adj.* Stale; sour; having an offensive odor or flavor.

ray | rā | —*noun* An ocean fish that has a flat body and a long, narrow tail that looks like a whip.

ray

red·coat | rĕd′ kōt | —*noun* A name for a British soldier during the American Revolution. The British soldiers wore bright red coats, making them easy targets for the colonists.

reed | rēd | —*noun* Any of several tall grasses or similar plants that have hollow stems.

ref·uge | rĕf yo͞oj | —*verb* Protection or shelter from danger.

reg·i·ment | rĕj′ ə mənt | —*noun* A unit of soldiers made up of two or more battalions.

reign | rān | —*verb* To rule or prevail over.

ridge | rĭj | —*noun* A long, narrow, raised strip or peak of something.

rig·ging | rĭg′ ĭng | —*noun* The arrangement of masts, sails, lines, and other equipment on a boat.

rigging

rise | rīz | —*noun* A gentle slope.

ru·in | ro͞o′ ĭn | —*verb* To destroy or damage; make useless or worthless.

ru·ins | ro͞o′ ĭnz | —*noun* The remains of a building or other structure or group of structures that has been destroyed or has fallen into pieces from age.

rush[1] | rŭsh | —*verb* 1. To move or act quickly; hurry. 2. To move or flow quickly with great force and noise.

rush[2] | rŭsh | —*noun* A grasslike plant that grows in marshes.

rus·tic | **rŭs′** tĭk | —*adj.* Simple; made of rough materials.

sand·bar | **sănd′** bär′ | —*noun* A ridge of sand built up by the action of waves or currents.

school | skōōl | —*noun* A large group of fish or other water animals swimming together.

scorn | skôrn | —*verb* To treat someone or something as worthless or bad; look down on.

se·dan | sĭ **dăn′** | —*noun* A type of portable enclosed chair for one person. It has poles on the front and the rear and is carried by two or more men.

sedan

sharp·en | **shär′** pən | —*verb* To make one more alert.

Shaw·nee | shô **nē′** | —*noun* A member of the Shawnee Indian tribe.

sheaves | shēvz | —*noun* Bundles of cut stalks of grain or similar plants bound with straw or twine.

sheaves

shrimp gum·bo | shrĭmp **gŭm′** bō | —*noun* A shrimp soup or stew thickened with okra.

skirt | skûrt | —*verb* To move or go around rather than across or through.

slave block | slāv blŏk | —*noun* A stand from which slaves were displayed and sold at a public auction.

snout | snout | —*noun* The long nose, jaws, or front part of the head of an animal.

so·ber | **sō′** ber | —*adj.* Serious; grave; solemn.

sole | sōl | —*noun* The bottom of a shoe or boot.

ă	pat	ĕ	pet
ā	pay	ē	be
â	care	ĭ	pit
ä	father	ī	pie
î	fierce	oi	oil
ŏ	pot	ŏŏ	book
ō	go	ōō	boot
ô	paw,	yōō	abuse
	for	ou	out
ŭ	cut	zh	vision
û	fur	ə	ago, item,
th	the		pencil, atom,
th	thin		circus
hw	which	ər	butter

so·nar | sō′ när′ | —*noun* A system that uses sound waves to discover underwater objects and find out where they are.

sow | sō | —*verb* To plant seed to grow a crop.

spin·ner·et | spĭn′ ə rĕt′ | —*noun* The part of a spider's body through which silky threads are produced.

spi·ral | spī′ rəl | —*noun* A curve that gradually widens as it coils around.

spire | spīr | —*noun* The top part of a steeple or other structure that tapers upward.

square | skwâr | —*verb* To set the jaw as if in a square.

squat | skwŏt | —*verb* To sit on one's heels, with the knees drawn close to one's chest.

stag | stăg | —*noun* A male deer that is fully grown.

Stamp Act | stămp ăkt | —*noun* A British law passed in 1765 requiring American colonists to pay a tax on all official documents and printed materials.

stead | stĕd | —*noun* The place or position usually occupied by another.

stu·di·ous | stoo′ dē əs | —*adj.* Earnest; serious and sincere.

sub·scrib·er | səb skrīb′ ər | —*noun* One who agrees to receive and pay for a certain number of issues of a publication.

suit | soot | —*verb* To be acceptable for.

sum·mons | sŭm′ ənz | —*noun* An order for someone to appear somewhere or to do something.

sun·shade | sŭn′ shād′ | —*noun* Something used as a protection from the sun, such as a parasol.

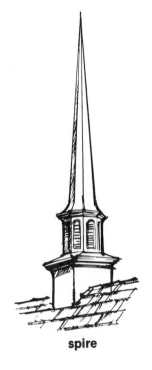

spire

stag

sus·tain | sə **stān′** | —*verb* To supply with needed food or supplies; to provide for.

sys·tem | sĭs′ təm | —*noun* An orderly way of doing something.

thatched | thăchd | —*adj.* Covered with straw, reeds, or palm fronds.

thatched

thong | thông | —*noun* A thin strip of leather used to fasten something, such as a sandal.

thresh | thrĕsh | —*verb* To separate the seeds or grain from a plant by striking or beating.

thong

trans·port | trăns **pôrt′** | or | trăns **pōrt′** | —*verb* To carry from one place to another.

ty·rant | tī′ rənt | —*noun* A ruler who uses power unjustly or cruelly.

ă	pat	ĕ	pet
ā	pay	ē	be
â	care	ĭ	pit
ä	father	ī	pie
î	fierce	oi	oil
ŏ	pot	o͞o	book
ō	go	o͞o	boot
ô	paw,	yo͞o	abuse
	for	ou	out
ŭ	cut	zh	vision
û	fur	ə	ago, item,
th	the		pencil, atom,
th	thin		circus
hw	which	ər	butter

un·hewn | un hyo͞on′ | —*adj.* Uncut; not felled.

u·ni·son | yo͞o′ nə sən | or | yo͞o′ nə zən | —*noun* A speaking of the same words at the same time.

up·ris·ing | ŭp′ rī zĭng | —*noun* A revolt or rebellion against authority.

up·wind | ŭp wĭnd′ | —*adv.* In the direction from which the wind blows.

vale | vāl | —*noun* A valley, often coursed by a stream; dale.

var·y·ing | vâr′ ē ing | —*adj.* Differing; a variety of.

vault | vôlt | —*noun* A room or compartment with strong walls and locks, used for keeping valuables safe.

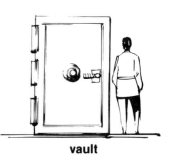

vault

vel·vet | věl′ vĭt | —*adj.* Smooth or soft as velvet.

ver·sion | vûr′ zhən | —*noun* A description or an account from one particular point of view.

ves·sel | věs′ əl | —*noun* A hollow container, such as a bowl, pitcher, jar, or tank, that can hold liquids.

vil·lain | vĭl′ ən | —*noun* A person or story character who is wicked or evil.

wake | wāk | —*noun* The path of waves, ripples, or foam left in the water by a moving boat or ship.

wick | wĭk | —*noun* A cord or piece of twisted thread in a candle or oil lamp. When it is lighted, the wick draws up the melted wax or oil to be burned.

wicker | wĭk′ ər | —*noun* Thin twigs or branches that bend easily. Wicker is used to make such things as baskets and light outdoor furniture.

wicker

wist·ful | wĭst′ fəl | —*adj.* Full of sad longing.

Yad·kin Riv·er | yăd′ kĭn rĭv′ ər | —*noun* A river in North Carolina.

Yan·kee | yăng′ kē | —*noun* A person from the northern part of the United States, especially a Union supporter or soldier in the Civil War.

Za·re·phath | zăr′ ə făth | —*noun* A Phoenician city, located between Tyre and Sidon, where Elijah lodged in the widow's house.

ă	pat	ĕ	pet
ā	pay	ē	be
â	care	ĭ	pit
ä	father	ī	pie
î	fierce	oi	oil
ŏ	pot	ŏŏ	book
ō	go	ōō	boot
ô	paw,	yōō	abuse
	for	ou	out
ŭ	cut	zh	vision
û	fur	ə	ago, item,
th	the		pencil, atom,
th	thin		circus
hw	which	ər	butter